IBO

THE ROOT OF
ALL HEALING

DANIEL BRETT

NOBLE**SAPIEN**

www.noblesapien.com

First published by NOBLE SAPIEN 2021

In writing Iboga: The Root of all Healing, the author has done his best to use the most current and accurate data available. As with any human endeavor, mistakes can be made, responsibility for which lies solely with the author, and not with those who assisted or are referenced in this work. If you spotted any egregious errors, please inform the author at

www.noblesapien.com.

First edition
ISBN: 978-1-8384462-1-5

This book was professionally typeset by Paul Baillie-Lane

Find out more at reedsy.com

To Mary, my mother, who taught me to ask questions.

To Robert, my father, who dared me to search for answers.

CONTENTS

IV ADDITIONAL INFORMATION

ACKNOWLEDGMENTS

Infinite love and gratitude to my family for the blind faith and ongoing support: Mary, Robert, Melanie, Kristian, Rob Jr, Lyndsay, Philip, Jake, and Grace Brett. And Brigid, Eric, Claire, and Mary Richards.

Thanks to my African hosts for graciously allowing me to observe their ceremonies and traditions. Nganga Papa Claver in Cameroon, and Ngangas Nima Mboka and Maduma Alexandre in Gabon. Yann Guignon for his work and guidance. And of course Hugues Obiang Poitevin AKA - "Tata Yo" at Ebando in Libreville.

Respect and thanks to Jeff Warren for the support, reading recommendations, and sage advice to rein in my focus. Thanks to Daniel Pinchbeck for the editing suggestions, Kash Khan at Educate Inspire Change for the feedback and support, Jamie McAlpin RN for walking me through some tricky cardiological data, Mike "Zappy" Zapolin for the faith, Kaia Roman for the feedback, and Jonathan Dickinson for heeding the call to serve, correcting my errors, and putting together the African journey of a lifetime.

Everlasting gratitude to Rebecca Washlow, whose time, support, partnership, and insights were invaluable. Enormous thanks to Heather Lundy, whose input was essential, and whose tips on toning it down resonated further than words on a page. Cheers to Ray Moss for sharing his design wizardry. Gratitude to Mary Smathers for the encouragement and practical publishing tips. Thanks to beta readers Kash

Khan, Vytas Groudis, Carla Kieffer, Nathan Teakle, Jill Hill, and Wimal Wijenayake for the manuscript feedback. Thanks to Joellen Hughes, for her friendship and for creating a space for me to wax lyrical at length. Cheers to Patrick Cooke, who showed me the only real artistic barometer is the stage. Undying love to Steve "Gandalf" Coan, who repaid me for spilling wine on his violin by pushing me down a rabbit hole. And of course, the legendary Matt Hazelton, for always being there as a friend, peer, cheerleader, tireless sounding board, and inspiring reminder to keep on keepin' on.

Honorable mentions include Michelle Vergara for the feedback and friendship, Erok (#### you) Holmberg for being Erok, Jeff Oddy for throwing me a lifeline when I needed it, Tim "Rise up" Cureton for the encouragement and cross-continental schlepping of manuscripts, Chris Johnson-Hill for the ongoing physical therapy, Jon Mangogna for the social coordinating, Dilara Ozkardesler for the baked goods, and Nick Fairman and Steve Reyer, just because.

Thanks to friends, and even strangers, who have helped from afar –Naveed Akram, Bruce K. Alexander, Kenneth Alper, Tony Audin, Shena Badena, Malcolm Baker, Nick Banegas, Dana Beal, Joshua Braun, Angie Cebulske, Mike Churchill, Jenna Cooke, Elizabeth Cundill, Paul Da Costa, Vanessa, Angela, and Monica Dimoff, Eric Dowling, Urusatvi Elena, Isabelle Geniet, Douglas Gilles, Ben Hill, Tony Hoare, Gonca Gul, Gunther Intelmann, Jon Paul Kahlan (JP), Elizabeth Kracht, Jordan Kronick, Ashley Laux, Ashley Ludman, Christine Marie, Gabor Mate, Trevor Millar, Preston Peet, Nadine Purdy, Nicole Regan, Paul Sevanich, Jon Simmonds, Santos Sitar, David Spitzer, and Christian and Theresa Thomson.

Cheers to the Boys from the Hood, AKA The Thunder####s, for keeping me amused: Steven Alldis, Robbie Atherton, Marc

Dobbing, Ben Holland, Matt Kearsley, Steve Lee, Nev and Adam Poole, James Rutland, Ben and Dan Silas, and Peter Tomlinson.

Gratitude and respect to the authors of the GITA (Global Ibogaine Therapy Alliance) protocols: Jonathan Dickinson, Jamie Mcalpin R.N. Clare Wilkins, Christine Fitzsimmons, Paige Guion R.N. Tanea Paterson, Douglas Greene. Bruno Rasmussen M.D. Jeffrey Kamlet M.D, DABAM, FASAM, and Roman Paskulin M.D. Ph.D.

Last but by no means least. Senor Darin McBratney. Supporter of the seemingly impossible, lightning rod for the ludicrous, psychedelic renegade, and friend whom I treasure like a bizarre, ultra-rare exotic pet. Without you this book would not have been conceived, never mind written.

And of course, to the "Spirit of Iboga" and other forces that have guided me throughout this work.

Basse!

I

IBOGA: THE SACRED WOOD

1

WHAT IS IBOGA?

"The more one is able to articulate what it is, the less others are able to understand."[1]

Terence Mckenna

"Challenging, beautiful, ineffable, humbling, enlightening, awe-inspiring, the Mount Everest of psychedelics," and above all, "healing." The descriptions ascribed to the iboga journey are many and have two things in common. First, they are all true. Second, they are a fumbling attempt to clothe in words an experience that transcends and probably predates human language. Articulating the true nature of the iboga journey is like trying to swim in the word 'ocean.' It offers an immersive glimpse into realms of being that defy rational explanation. It facilitates modes of consciousness that leave one convinced that truth is indeed stranger than fiction. It reveals domains that exist so far beyond the scope of modern scientific discourse as to demand we rethink what consciousness, knowledge, and existence really mean, in turn fostering a humble acceptance for the limits of human understanding.

Therein lies the problem with the question "What is iboga"? In the absence of any satisfactory definition, and in the unlikely event the psychedelic "peak experience" is explained anytime soon, the answer will depend on who you ask.

3

A Bwiti shaman or *nganza* may talk of a super-sentient being tasked with instructing humankind on the nature of life, death, the natural world, self-actualization, and primarily – healing. Although they may look fondly on iboga's arrival in the west, some (but not all) may question the practice of strip mining the root bark in search of the single ibogaine alkaloid, thus affecting the plant's raw, holistic power. Others may refrain from answering at all or simply state that full understanding of the plant's potential is beyond the grasp of the uninitiated.

Answers from first-world, kick-seeking twenty-somethings may range from "an acrid root that just made me vomit for fifteen hours" to "a life-changing, hi-definition dream machine that smashed open my receiver, accessed some ultra-weird transmission frequencies, flipped the narratives I told myself about myself, and lifted the veil on the true purpose of existence."

In an honest moment, an opioid-peddling pharma CEO may describe iboga as a rabble-rouser threatening to blast a hole in share prices.

In contrast, a recovering heroin addict may describe iboga as the gatekeeper between the gutter and the stars, a pragmatic poet-warrior that landed a knockout punch from a velvet glove. When they awoke and the stars quit spinning, they realized iboga had rendered dope sickness a bad memory, returned them to a pre-addicted state, armed them with the tools needed to create a life, and changed the story they told themselves about themselves.

Howard Lotsof was one such addict. In 1962, Lotsof, a 19-year-old New Yorker experimented with ibogaine. As the plant's effects began to subside, it dawned on him that the usual withdrawal symptoms of heroin were gone. Lotsof had inadvertently become the first to experience ibogaine's capacity to interrupt addiction. It was from this discovery that whispers of the compound began to slowly permeate western medical parlance.

Lotsof went on to become a pioneer of ibogaine research and is widely credited as the founding father of ibogaine therapy in treating substance abuse. His devotion to the plant continued until his death in 2010. Before his passing, he described iboga as *"a laser-guided smart missile for trauma"* that *"takes you right to the issues you have to deal with and allows you to deal with them in a detached manner."* [2]

SO WHAT IS IBOGA?

The word "iboga" (occasionally spelled eboka or eboga) comes from the Tsogo verb *boghaga* meaning "to care for," and refers to plants that contain the ibogaine alkaloid. [3] Chief among these is the Central African rain forest shrub: Tabernanthe Iboga.

The Tabernanthe Iboga tree is native to a bio-region of West-Central Africa that includes Gabon and a few Congo Basin areas. Here, it grows on the moist, semi-shaded rain forest floor. It produces green leaves, pink and white flowers, and inedible, oval-shaped orange fruits. However, its real claim to fame is the potent psychoactive alkaloids contained in its bitter-tasting root bark.

Long before western medical pioneers hailed iboga as a phar-maceutical miracle, its mysterious healing properties and capac-ity to trigger intense, crystal-clear visionary experiences were the keystone of a west African spiritual practice later named "Bwiti." Members of this animist nature culture venerate the plant as a medicine, a key to the spirit realm, a channel to deceased ances-tors, and a tuning fork for the mind, body, and spirit.

In smaller quantities, a spoon of iboga stimulates the central nervous system, boosting energy and alertness. Bwiti members claim it sharpens their hunting skills and keeps them attentive, energetic, and dialed in during ceremonial rituals.[4]

For upcoming Bwiti initiates, a single spoon of iboga will be the first of many. These mammoth doses, administered incrementally during prolonged initiation and healing ceremonies, are known to induce symbolic death, expedite radical spiritual transformation, cure pathological illnesses and stabilize both the family and community structure. After consumption, people report slipping deep into an oneirogenic (dream-like) state of consciousness. Here, many encounter lucid visions, repressed memories, insights into the nature of existence, and much more. These insights are considered invaluable to the well-being of both the initiate and the larger Bwiti culture.

ORIGIN TALES

The true story of iboga's relationship with humans is lost to antiquity. Archaeological findings indicate iboga use in the Congo Basin stretches back at least two thousand years.[5] Over time, various origin tales have emerged that differ depending on which Bwiti sect tells the story.

One legend speaks of a hunter arriving to find a trapped porcupine gnawing at the root bark of a large shrub. He takes the iboga-loaded creature home, cooks it, eats it, and the visions begin. After his journey, he claims to understand things with an impossible clarity. The disbelief of his clansmen prompts a return journey to the shrub. The root bark was harvested and consumed. His claims were verified, and the plant worship tradition was born.

As recorded by ethnographer James W. Fernandez, another myth speaks of a heaven in which God wonders why he has never seen a black man. Concluding they were too sinful to gain access, he takes pity and decides to help them. God kills a pygmy, brings him to heaven, cuts off a finger and toe, and plants these appendages in the forest as iboga seedlings.

God informs the pygmy that anyone who eats iboga will arrive in heaven after death. He then places the pygmy's bones in a stream, where the pygmy's wife discovers them during a fishing trip. A wildcat steals the bones. The wife follows the creature to its lair. Here, she is greeted by a voice instructing her to eat from the bush growing at the cave's mouth. As the plant's effects take hold, her dead husband appears before her. He claims he has returned to spread a powerful new African religion, the chief sacrament being a plant that allows its eaters to meet with departed ancestors.[6]

FORBIDDEN FRUIT

Nowadays, many anthropologists concur that the biblical Genesis story, in its original format, was a tale passed down orally by hunter-gatherer tribes to describe events that took place over tens, if not hundreds of thousands of years. Essentially, it was the tale of humankind's multi-millennia transition from homo simpleton to homo sapien. Later, when writing emerged in Mesopotamia around 5-6000 years ago, the condensed, twisted, heavily edited version of this tale was written into the cultural record by the newly emerged, post-agricultural land-owning classes to terrify the agricultural workers into subservience.

The "Fertile Crescent" of Mesopotamia, where hunter-gatherers eventually settled and began to farm, became The Garden of Eden. The transition from nomadic living to farming became expulsion from paradise. The punishment dished out to Adam, of 'toiling in the fields,' became the whip to keep agricultural laborers in check. The birth of modern civilization, which required hunter-gatherers' expulsion from the land to make way for agriculture, became the triumph of Cain (the citizen) over Abel (the nomad).

Underlying it all was the cognitive revolution (the fruit of knowledge) when the human brain ballooned, an event that still today leaves evolutionary biologists confusedly scratching their disproportionately large heads.

The only thing we know for sure about this mysterious evolutionary period is that our brains got real big, real quick. While creationists may cry foul, it's reasonable to conclude that a nootropic apple, declared off-limits by some prankster God was not to blame. Yet still, why and how the cognitive revolution occurred remains a mystery.

Hypotheses include environmental pressures, cooked meat, a means of survival in larger and more complex social groups, alien intervention, all of the above, none of the above, and more. Then, there's Terrence McKenna's 'Stoned Ape' theory.

Although his book, *Food of the Gods,* made brief mention of iboga as a potential candidate for the brain-boosting *fruit of knowledge*, it was quickly overlooked in favor of the Psilocybe Cubensis mushroom. Given humankind's African origins, is it such a leap to think iboga may have facilitated our first psychedelic experiences? Considering a minority of Bwitists incorporate certain Judeo-Christian doctrines, it's understandable that some sects pinpoint Tabernanthe Iboga as the original "fruit of knowledge."

Could they be correct? Was McKenna too hasty in dismissing iboga as a candidate for this mythical object? Was Central Western Africa the Garden of Eden? If so, could Tabernanthe

Iboga have been the catalyst for the human cognitive revolution? Perhaps the best group to ask might be the iboga-eating, tool using gorillas of the Gabonese rain forest. But they can't talk, right?[7]

Koko was a female western lowland gorilla with an IQ reportedly equal to that of a human infant, whose ability to communicate with her keepers via sign language captured the public imagination.[8] Before her 2018 passing, Koko had mastered over a thousand sign language statements. She was able to formulate coherent sentences and communicate wants, needs, and thoughts.[9] Although the captive Koko never ate iboga, we know for certain that her free-roaming family of the Gabon jungle definitely did, and still does.[10]

EASIER DONE THAN SAID

While the natural sciences may speak of alkaloids, chemical structures, and the neurological switches iboga is thought to flick, the mechanics of the visionary, psycho-spiritual effects remain the domain of hypothesis and educated guesswork. In other words: we have little clue. For every question answered, hundreds more are posed. This limits the discussion to what is known, what is theorized, and that which clearly exists despite its continued capacity to buck rational understanding.

Readers of *The Hitchhiker's Guide to the Galaxy* by the late Douglas Adams may recall a fictional, inconceivably quirky creature named the "Babelfish." Upon inserting the Babelfish into one's ear, it acts as a universal translator that seamlessly bridges the language gap between the countless species of beings inhabiting the cosmos. Adams describes the creature as "possibly the oddest thing in the universe."

Echoing William Paley's "watchmaker analogy," The Hitchhiker's Guide notes that the evolutionary odds of a creature as useful and technologically adept as the Babelfish occurring naturally are: zero. In Adam's book, God is depicted as a being who refuses to reveal his existence, claiming that proof denies faith, and without faith, he is nothing. Unfortunately for God, his Babelfish masterwork constitutes irrefutable evidence of intelligent design. Thus, according to his own rationale, God cannot exist. "Doh," says God and promptly vanishes in a "puff of logic."[11]

In this context, the Babelfish story serves as a lighthearted metaphor reflecting the problems in accounting for something as penetrating and profound as iboga. Was iboga a mere product of evolutionary coincidence? Or was it "intelligently designed" and delivered to catalyze 'communion'?

In efforts to explain how nature could have assembled a plant that seems custom-engineered to achieve such results, materialist scientists may cite evolutionary trial and error, coincidence, and blind chance. They may argue that reports of bizarre visions can be chalked up to the actions of an obscure alkaloid bonding with certain neurotransmitters in a manner yet to be understood.

In contrast, those returning from an iboga journey, and struggling to reconcile with a recent visit from deceased relatives, a crystal-clear recollection of their divine nature, and witnessing a high-definition movie recounting the creation of the universe from the atomic level up, may argue such conclusions to be naive and intellectually vain.

A neutral observer may interject that as iboga's popularity increases, so does the likelihood of unsupported claims due to the experience's unimaginable nature. The matter is further obfuscated because iboga occupies a unique and traditionally mutually exclusive overlap point where the world of hard drug addicts intersects with spiritual pilgrims.

WHAT IBOGA(INE) IS NOT

A Magic Bullet

Ibogaine is the most powerful addiction interrupter currently known to science. However, the slew of sensationalist media reports hailing it as a one-shot "miracle cure" for addiction are at best misleading, and at worst, dangerously deceitful. Lauding it as such cheapens what a powerful compound it actually is.

Addiction is a complex, multi-layered issue that requires tackling on numerous levels. Research, anecdotal reports, and case studies conclude that in the absence of a strong personal will, an adequate social support system, and a professional administration that understands the importance of aftercare, many addicts will return to substance abuse even after iboga(ine) treatment.

An apt analogy may be to liken a recovering addict to a person recently released from a long period of incarceration. Iboga represents the key to their cell door, or at least their parole hearing. Once on the outside, it's up to them to implement the steps required to remain in the free world. Progress is often much easier for individuals with an understanding support network of friends, family, and professional care.

The same applies to those who undertake iboga journeys for therapeutic assistance. Although iboga is eminently capable of revealing underlying psychological issues, it can't simply reverse the effects of traumatic events. It can, however, help reframe them more positively, shine a powerful light on the work necessary to achieve one's objectives, and provide a clearer mental map from which to implement change. Much like addiction, this may best be enacted with the support of a strong social network, psychotherapist, or both.

Savior to the Opioid Epidemic

The current global opioid epidemic is largely a result of the community, cultural, and spiritual vacuum left in the wake of centuries of rampant materialism, conscienceless free markets, and the emergence of a capitalist culture that leaves countless millions in the cold. Unquestionably, ibogaine can play a role in helping individuals beat their personal addiction problems. However, claims regarding iboga's power to combat the current addiction crisis fail to account for the true driving factors behind this monstrous epidemic.

That said, if used correctly, iboga may serve to help direct the tide of human consciousness down a road where the toxic wasteland in which addictive tendencies flourish appears in the rearview mirror. This possibility will be explored later in this book.

Solely for Addicts

A few decades ago, the Western iboga conversation remained largely confined to maverick medical practitioners, hardcore psychonauts, off-map travelers, and heroin addicts. Since then, media giants from Fox News to Rolling Stone magazine have jumped on board the iboga reportage bandwagon.[12, 13] In a perfect world, these headlines would talk of a sacred plant, which, if respected, were known to bestow healing, mental clarity, and a road map to personal liberation. Sadly, the media mentions these revelatory gifts only in the context of the opioid crisis.

Consequently, *"Iboga isn't for me because I'm not an addict"* is a phrase many in the iboga community are familiar with. Iboga's use for purposes of ceremony, healing, initiation, and community bonding likely dates back before the word "addiction" entered either the European or African lexicon. To claim that iboga's potential is limited to its anti-addiction properties is an enormous mistruth. The gifts bestowed on individuals who seek iboga's psycho-spiritual offerings can be just as valuable as those bestowed on the addict.

A Recreational Party Drug

Small doses of iboga may enhance one's mood. However, physical discomfort, purging, lack of physical coordination, limited availability, prolonged duration, high cost, and disagreeable short-term side effects are only some of the reasons the words "party" and "iboga" don't go well together. Thrill-seekers and weekend warriors are advised to search elsewhere.

100% Safe

Although ibogaine-related fatalities are extremely scarce they have still been recorded. A number of these have taken place in private, clinical, or pseudo-clinical settings. Thanks to the work from a dedicated core of medical professionals, recent years have witnessed the emergence of reliable data aimed at recognizing at-risk individuals before it's too late. Subsequent chapters will discuss this topic in greater detail.

For Everyone

There's a good reason academic researchers pre-screen, monitor, assist and counsel volunteers prior, during, and after their psychedelic experience. Anyone with a history of severe mental illness should think hard about signing up for the iboga experience.

At the time of writing, iboga is not available in clinical research environments currently experimenting with LSD and psilocybin et al. Anyone thinking of experiencing iboga must weigh the decision themselves. The recommended criteria on which to do this will be explored in later chapters.

A Solitary Journey

Iboga(ine) won't prevent you from needing the bathroom. It may, however, prevent you from arriving there unassisted in one piece. One of the side effects of iboga(ine) is Ataxia. Although not dangerous in itself, ataxia may make physical movement difficult. Landing face down on the ground, possibly injured, is an unpleasant prospect regardless of where one's head is at. However, physical injuries during an iboga journey may be the stuff of nightmares. A high dose of iboga should not be taken alone, but rather in the company of trusted allies and those familiar with overseeing, and if necessary, providing physical assistance to the subject during their journey. A trip to equatorial Africa to undertake a Bwiti initiation is outside the reach of many seekers. However, there is a growing number of seasoned individuals in the west trained to safely maximize the experience. Where possible, seek these people out.

Finally, it is with good reason that the word "intention" appears so frequently throughout psychedelic discourse. It is advised that anyone who wishes to experience the immense power of iboga define and justify their reasons and goals in advance. Altruism, personal growth, and a desire to help shape oneself into a vehicle for positive social change are great places to start. These well-intentioned driving factors constitute the correct motivational terrain on which the spirit of iboga lovingly embraces those who choose to meet it there.

2

THE PREPARATIONS

As iboga's popularity grows, so does the confusion regarding what iboga is and what it is not. This confusion extends to the differences between iboga and ibogaine, and what purpose the different compositions best serve.

The preparations noted in this chapter are (1) Root Bark, (2) TA (Total Alkaloid), and (3) Ibogaine HCL (Hydrochloride). In some (but not all) cases, the psychological and physiological effects may vary depending on which alkaloids the different preparations contain.

Much of the following information stems from reports from the ibogaine medical subculture. Their work has been crucial to providing an overview regarding both therapy strategies and general outlines as to what to expect from the different preparations.

ROOT BARK

The root bark of the Tabernanthe Iboga plant is just as it sounds. TA (Total Extract) and ibogaine hydrochloride (HCL) are both derivatives of this raw material. After removal from the ground, the root bark is shaved and consumed either in whole form or ground into a powder and eaten or drank. This is how Bwiti sects have been ingesting the alkaloids since before records began. In a western setting, the root bark is eaten almost exclusively by users seeking a non-medical, 'psycho-spiritual' experience.

Root bark is traditionally consumed in smaller doses, building up to increased amounts throughout the journey. It is digested and metabolized more slowly than other preparations, resulting in an experience that 'takes hold' more gradually and lasts for a longer period. Its relatively small ratio of psychoactive alkaloids to inert materials means the volume of material necessary to trigger a deep experience may cause physical discomfort levels less common with TA or HCL.

Root bark occasionally induces vomiting. Many attest these purgative effects contribute to the overall experience and that purging adds a crucial spiritual component, particularly in the latter stages of their iboga journey. They say this is iboga's way of ensuring one's vehicle is tuned, free of excess drag, and primed for the journey. However, many providers feel that these discomfort levels make root bark an impractical choice for substance abuse patients and instead use ibogaine HCL. Nevertheless, some use root bark as a supplementary treatment or as a booster measure when the effects of an HCL treatment begin to subside. Additionally, root barks' gentle effects in smaller doses make it a good candidate for introducing the subject to the plant.

TA (TOTAL ALKALOID)

Although the ibogaine alkaloid takes the spotlight, it is but one of many alkaloids present in the root bark. Total Alkaloid Extract is the net product of separating ibogaine and all the other alkaloids from the inert, non-psychoactive materials in the root bark. Many who have undergone a TA experience say that ingesting the full spectrum of alkaloids significantly improves both the comfort and clarity of their journey. A suitable analogy may be to think of ibogaine as the lead violin dropping mind-blowing melodies center stage, and the other iboga alkaloids as the orchestra tasked with enhancing the overall sound.

Purified TA extract contains high concentrations of ibogaine and may induce a stronger experience than a HCL dose. It is presumed that this results from the other alkaloids working to amplify and enhance ibogaine's effects. Although their precise actions are unclear, some of these alkaloids have been shown to act on the same neurotransmitter sites as ibogaine.[14]

Most medical providers feel HCL is best suited to treating addiction. In contrast, some TA proponents assert that TA provides the best of both worlds: reducing physical discomfort while still imparting the plant's full spirit, thus making it suitable for both addiction interruption and a deeper psycho-spiritual journey.

Although rarer, a few providers claim a TA/HCL mix is a powerful and highly beneficial combination for addiction treatment. This approach involves administering a measured quantity of HCL to the subject during a TA journey. Some providers say this method tends to extend the psycho-spiritual component, create an increase in noribogaine conversion, and offers an effective way of adding depth without time to the journey. Alternatively, TA preparations are used by certain providers as a "booster" supplement following an acute HCL detoxification dose.

Ibogaine Hydrochloride (HCL)

Outside of the traditional ceremonial environment, and particularly in clinical settings, ibogaine HCL is by far the most commonly administered iboga derivative. The extraction procedure filters out the other alkaloids, resulting in the purest known form of ibogaine, which appears as either a clear solution or white crystals.

The comparative ease with which it can be studied, measured, and thus adjusted for gender, body weight, and desired results makes ibogaine HCL the medicine of choice for treating substance addiction. HCL metabolizes more rapidly and easily than other iboga preparations, resulting in a quicker onset and a shorter recovery period. Its potency requires the user to consume far lesser quantities of material than with TA or root bark. This is thought to be a key factor in reducing both physical discomfort and purgative effects.

NORIBOGAINE

Noribogaine is technically a "derivative" of iboga. However, it's not one to be found listed on any provider's menu.

Noribogaine (12-hydroxy-ibogamine) is ibogaine's principal psychoactive metabolite, and is a powerful selective serotonin uptake inhibitor (SSRI).[15] In Layman's terms, this means it functions similarly to many prescription anti-depressants; by prolonging serotonin activity in the brain.

After iboga consumption, Noribogaine is produced in the user's liver and then transmitted into the bloodstream, where it is thought to linger for some time.[16] These actions are believed to play a significant role in the long-term suppression of cravings for harmful substances.[17] Following treatment, many report feelings of well-being, along with zero cravings for toxins ranging from coffee to crack cocaine. These symptoms are thought to be attributable to the presence of noribogaine in their bloodstream.

3

THE JOURNEY

Let's assume the day has finally arrived. If you're embarking on addiction treatment, let's also assume your electrocardiogram test (ECG) and liver test has confirmed vital organs are good to go. You're hydrated, suitably nourished, and the opioids or other drugs have left your system. (More about this later).

If your upcoming initiation takes place in the jungles of Gabon, you're now dressed in a loincloth, and covered in body and face paint. You've been washed and purified in a river or waterfall, and you've undergone a period of fasting, abstinence, and other components of the pre-initiation apprenticeship.

Alternatively, you've neither traveled to Africa, nor is your decision to experience iboga related to addiction. Rather, you've chosen to receive iboga's psycho-spiritual benefits in a retreat center or the like.

Addicts will likely now be given a test dose, a single small measurement of ibogaine administered a few hours before the main course in order to check for potential allergic and/or metabolic reactions.[18] Similarly, those in a ceremonial setting may be given smaller measurements of iboga.

Soon thereafter, the doses increase. Around the corner awaits a deeply profound journey into realms of consciousness and possibly supernatural terrain stranger than one could possibly imagine. If anxiety sets in, remember that iboga is your ally. Its job is to help, at which it's an expert. This is a good time to reaffirm one's intentions. If a letter of intent has been written, or any questions one wishes to ask iboga, this is an excellent time to revise. Remember why you came and what you're there to achieve. Remember that everyone's experience is different. Forget imagined comparisons with LSD, mushrooms, or any other psychedelics. Forget what you have heard, read, or what you think you know, and be flexible with your expectations. Soon enough, you'll realize that the medicine is in the driver's seat and knows precisely where it's headed.

BE NOT AFRAID

When Terence McKenna coined his famous phrase about the benefits of "*not giving into astonishment,*" he was referring to DMT.[19] However, this brilliant observation remains an essential travel tip for the iboga journey. Many report the moment the decision is made to step up, compose oneself, and replace fear with courage is the moment that the journey takes on a new meaning. Anxiety or dread gives way to an ecstatic sense of what is truly possible.

Despite iboga's power, many people report a degree of control over the experience. This is not acid or anything else which can drag one helplessly down an uncomfortable and sometimes terrifying psychological hole. Iboga is no lottery in which Heaven or Hell is decided by the flip of a coin. It may be in the pilot's seat, but it may invite the subject to co-pilot. Providing it deems one's chosen course to be beneficial, it may also be open to suggestions. Try asking. The answer may surprise you.

If an experience is too much to handle, it may be discontinued by issuing a firm mental directive to "make it stop."[20] The same may be achieved by opening the eyes or removing the eye mask. This may sound strange. However, once immersed in the journey, one's barometer of 'strange' will take on entirely different dimensions.

Essentially, it is a mistake to allow fear-based preconceptions to dissuade one from experiencing iboga. That said, remember that once the journey begins, you're entering terrain that psychedelic philosophers have likened to the mythical hero's journey. Tales about Buddha, Jesus, even Luke Skywalker all share this common and timeless theme. It's only after the subject has faced down their fears that they emerge the hero. Subsequently, if something is encountered that makes one's hair stand on end, the optimal course of action may be to face it and remind oneself that the toughest steel is forged in the hottest flames.

THE LAUNCH SEQUENCE

In the absence of solid descriptive language, providers have come to loosely refer to the iboga journey in terms of three stages. These are the "acute" or "oneirophrenic" stage, followed respectively by the "evaluative" and "residual stimulation" phases. Although helpful, such labels are a vague attempt to convey overlapping elements that vary from subject to subject and depend on timing, dose, metabolism, and other factors.

The first signs that iboga is taking effect are largely physical and often uncomfortable. As one's heart rate drops, it's a matter of time before physical disorientation and confusion sets in. If you're not yet vertical, now is the time to lie down. As ataxia (loss of motor skills) sets in, the only reason to rise should be for an accompanied trip to the bathroom if required.

Iboga's initial effects appear in increasingly powerful waves. As it gradually floods the system, some may begin to feel the composure they spent all week meditating to achieve begin to crumble against the overwhelming, albeit temporary, weight of the experience. Telling oneself to relax in the face of rising panic is easier said than done. A more suitable mantra may be to "let go" and simply surrender. Often, this surrender marks the point where iboga begins to unveil its immense capabilities. So, let go, and enjoy the ride.

For addicts, the absence of physical withdrawal symptoms will become apparent anywhere between 30 minutes and 2 hours into the journey. This observation (the realization that one's addiction has been ejected from the driver's seat) will hopefully bring joy, astonishment, and the perfect mindset with which to ride out what's about to begin. It's time to strap in, close one's eyes, and enjoy the fireworks.

THE ACUTE STAGE

The acute stage is the time for probing memories, intellectual and emotional soul-searching, and inner reflection. It's also the time of visions.

In normal waking consciousness, the appearance of closed eye visuals can nearly always be chalked up to either traces of recently encountered bright lights, blood cells moving through the retina's blood vessels, or some other form of readily explainable retinal activity. However, the realm one is entering is anything but normal waking consciousness, and nothing therein is readily explainable. This is the waking dream state, where the show usually begins. A little later in the journey, it may be that the visions become easier to wrap one's head around. In the meantime, drop any preconceptions. Expect both the unexpected and possibly the unfathomably weird.

Visuals may appear from nowhere, projected onto one's inner eyelids in all manner of strange shapes and forms, from figures and faces clamoring for attention, to film stock memories, vast landscapes, through to the majestic, ghoulish, absurd, utterly cartoonish, and even mundane. Alternately, one may witness an impossibly rapid, panoramic viewing of one's entire memory bank, perceived contact with entities, or other staggeringly profound elements.[21]

Initially, the form and function of these visions may appear blurry. Such visual decomposition is usually temporary. Although timing depends on the individual, these images should eventually coalesce into lucid, structured visions, which may be distinguishable from regular dreams by their malleability and their dissolution upon opening one's eyes. At this stage, it's not uncommon for people to report the looming presence of an audible, oscillating buzzing sound. More about that later.

THE EVALUATIVE STAGE

Metaphorically speaking, the first phase could be likened to performing a computer malware scan. In order to identify and deal with unwelcome intruders, the software must perform an exhaustive search of the system's hard drive.

By whichever mysterious means iboga cracks open and scours one's memory bank, its purpose is to identify threats. It begins by sorting through the vast deposits of mental debris accumulated over a lifetime. The net result of this fishing expedition should be a round-up of psychological villains all neatly herded into a single holding cell. In this case, the 'villains' are the traumatic memories and major events that would go on to influence choices and behavioral patterns. When the post-scan pop-up box appears asking whether to "remove all identified threats," the beginning of the second phase could be likened to clicking 'yes.'

When eradicating computer viruses, it's unnecessary that the user understands the volume or nature of identifiable threats. The human psyche is infinitely more complex. To effectively free oneself from the influence of these psychic scoundrels, iboga and traditional psychotherapy are on the same page: They demand the explorer know their enemy and agree that successfully disassociating from these elements is best achieved by getting up-close-and-personal for an objective review. Both treatments utilize an 'evaluative' examination of the origins, nature, and reach of these events. Hence, the second phase of the journey is named the 'evaluative' stage.

During this period, subjects report that the information, epiphanies, and realizations appear in formats ranging from the familiar (such as audio and visual) to the indescribably unfamiliar, including downloads from other realms. Although the experience varies from subject to subject, it's commonly reported this phase can provide a deep cognitive understanding of major personal issues and a received awareness of how to go about modifying one's future behavior, particularly in regard to navigating the minefield of addiction.

To many, the idea of staring down a line-up of one's long-held, deeply rooted psychological foes and traumatic memories may inspire dread. However, subjects commonly report such feelings are buffered by a sense of emotional objectivity.

In a traditional therapeutic setting, the emergence of painful memories may be accompanied by deep emotion. On iboga, many claim such fears are absent, allowing them to interact, 'evaluate,' and relive the event in a detached manner.

This period may last anywhere from 8-20 hours. On a practical note, it's worth remembering that one's current state of mind could be likened to that of extremely deep meditation. Regardless of one's depth, it's still possible to become distracted. Subsequently, it's important to be in a setting where the chances of disturbance by external stimuli such as light and noise are minimal, preferably zero.

THE RESIDUAL STIMULATION STAGE

Eventually, the acute effects of iboga begin to gradually subside. Consciousness levels fluctuate, and the subject becomes increasingly aware of their surroundings and external stimuli. Mobility may remain an issue for a few hours, and you may feel uncomfortable and tired. Despite the dream-like nature of the experience, you have still lost a night's sleep, and there's little chance of dozing off anytime soon. In the days that follow, some report a diminished appetite for sleep.

WHAT NOW?

Although diminished, the effects of iboga now appear in more subtle ways. This is a great time to reflect on one's journey. You may feel tired and utterly washed out. You may also feel euphoric and amazed that an obscure alkaloid from an African root was indeed able to match the bold claims you'd heard or read about.

At this point, the spirit of iboga is still working hard on your behalf. This is particularly the case for addicts. If iboga(ine) did its job, they should now be experiencing heightened clarity, alertness, motivation, and a readiness to face the world head-on, drug-free, with renewed vigor and purpose. They have unlocked their cell door, and the possibility of freedom from addiction has never seemed so tangible. However, for convenience sake, let's assume the prison is located in a vast, unfamiliar forest. They may be out of their cell. They are not out of the woods. Successfully navigating oneself clear of the forest will require planning, discipline, and intent. It will require aftercare. This will be further explored in a later chapter.

BOOSTER DOSES

Many providers attest to the benefits of continued administration of smaller doses of iboga or ibogaine, particularly in cases where the patient has a long history of drug dependency. In the days and weeks that follow, it is thought that booster doses can be highly effective in treating residual cravings, unresolved psychological issues, and to prolong iboga or ibogaine's therapeutic benefits.[22]

4

THE DREAM MACHINE

"Our normal waking consciousness, rational consciousness as we call it, is but one special type of consciousness, whilst all about it, parted from it by the filmiest of screens, there lie potential forms of consciousness entirely different." [23]

William James

Spiritual practices can be as diverse as their practitioners. Whether it be quiet contemplation, holotropic breathing, sound bathing, sensory deprivation, or any other method, the aim is usually the same; to trade active thinking for inward focus, thus arriving at a state of acute mental clarity and calm.

For a smaller, rarer group of practitioners, this mezzanine of consciousness is merely the first step towards what they consider meditation's ultimate destination. It is a state described by Timothy Leary as "complete transcendence – beyond words, beyond space–time," or by disciples of Eastern religions as a complete loss of attachment to a separate sense of self. [24, 25]

In attempts to articulate this elusive experience, many users describe it as feeling "at one with the entire universe." This obscure concept may seem reserved for gurus and spiritual elites. However, iboga, which has long been revered as a fast-track means of inducing this state, changes everything.

Newcomers to this realm may think they have arrived in uncharted and utterly bizarre terrain. In fact, it has been known for thousands of years. It has been called the realm of the eternal, of archetypes, timelessness, and the collective unconscious. It is the realm where the 'waking dreams' for which iboga is famed begin to appear. It is the realm of visions.

These may include mystical states, alternate dimensions, entities, long-buried personal episodes from one's past, and ethereal dreamscapes. Some report encountering bizarre scenes so far removed from everyday experience as to render them indescribable. One thing the visions seem to have in common is that they appear as real, if not more "real" than real life.

Beyond Virtual Reality

The visionary stage of the iboga journey has been compared to watching a movie unfold in the mind's eye. In this case, the mind's eye may be as clear as watching 3D cinema. Or, better yet, a live theater production, or even an actor on stage. Specifics aside, these ultra-lucid, real-time revelations often appear with a level of clarity, immersion, and narrative flow that the modern Virtual Reality industry could only dream of emulating. Beyond the visual components, expect words, sounds, light bulb moments of solar intensity, psychic downloads, and other mediums capable of shattering the imagination.

Sometimes, visions are framed and conveyed in themes that resonate with the subject's background. Global travelers may witness an airport departure screen offering a range of cosmic locations. Tech workers may run into Alan Turing patiently waiting to ruminate on the future of artificial intelligence. Philosophy students may find themselves embroiled in a lively discussion with Spinoza, or Plato, or both. Bwiti members also report that the visionary components and their consequent interpretation sometimes stem from their own cultural conditioning. A minority of Bwiti sects are Christian and report meeting Judeo-Christian entities, including Jesus.

Regardless of language, creed, religious leanings, or cultural background, reports often share elements too similar to be casually dismissed as a neurological coincidence. It is these elements the following material will attempt to address.

The following audiovisual dramas are commonly categorized as the pinnacle of the psychedelic journey. In Abraham Maslow's famous hierarchy of needs, "self-actualization" sits at the apex of the pyramid. According to Maslow, peak transcendental experiences have the potential to act as a powerful aid towards self-actualization. Not only do the visions outlined herein conform to Maslow's "peak experience" criteria, but many confirm they indeed played a key role in kick-starting the self-actualization process Maslow believed vital for personal transformation.

DISCLAIMER

Iboga is one of the most powerful natural visionary triggers known to exist. During a high-dose iboga journey, the chance of being privy to a true "peak experience" is higher than on other compounds (DMT notwithstanding). Nevertheless, it depends on set, setting, dose, and innumerable other key factors. Just because the visions and sensory elements outlined herein are a common occurrence does not mean they are universally experienced. The iboga journey is different for everyone. Many people have profound visionary experiences. Some do not.

While reading, it's important to remain mindful that the mysteries of the subject, combined with the highly personal nature of the experience, render these descriptions anecdotal and subjective. In the opening chapter of this book, it was written that one cannot swim in the word "ocean." It's only natural that anyone preparing to embark on an iboga journey would wish to devour every piece of relevant literature. However, the difference between academic knowledge and actual experience is profound.

Finally, considering the visual terrain accessed by iboga is practically limitless, to condense iboga's visionary menu only to that which follows would be grossly reductive. In simple terms, that means to expect anything, including:

None of What is Listed Below

To those thinking about experiencing iboga, some would argue it is unwise to read the following descriptions. Doing so may give rise to preconceptions and expectations, thus setting them up for potential disappointment if and when such things fail to appear. What follows may best serve as an interesting read for those who wish to learn about iboga but no wish to participate. Alternatively, it may offer validation to those who have experienced iboga, witnessed these things, and seek reassurance that they're not alone in their ensuing wonderment.

Oscillating Buzz

Although this component is auditory rather than visual, the presence of a buzzing sound is too commonly recalled to ignore.[26] Although occasionally reported to manifest as a tingling in the skin, most experience it as an intense, palpable sound wave. Although it may feel and sound intense, very rarely is it said to cause discomfort or present any sort of threat.

Bwiti members claim this noise is the vibrational frequency of a separate plane of existence. This dimension, they say, is the domain of spirits.[27] In the wake of this experience, many users are left convinced that this soul-shaking, utterly alien noise can only stem from supernatural realms. But that's another conversation.

Other descriptions include a loud oscillatory dial tone or a drawn-out, a chant-like bass frequency that fluctuates between dull and sharp, or as the kind of penetrating buzz from a close flyby by an enormous winged insect, echoing Carlos Castaneda's description of *"a fly as the guardian between two worlds."*[28]

It is said that this 'buzz' becomes audible during moments when the journey changes gears, intensifies, and the subject experiences a marked increase in the sensation of physical and mental vibration. Many have likened it to a psychic "frequency booster," or a carrier wave that acts as a vibratory propellant to one's destination.

It has been hypothesized that this sound wave may correspond with a shift in attentional resources between the brain's two hemispheres.[29] Dr. Carl Anderson speculates that the noise may kick start the process of "bihemispheric reintegration" between the right and left parts of the brain and act as a key component in iboga's addiction-busting capability.[30] If true, one can't help wondering whether the creators of audio systems such as 'Hemi-Sync,' whose products reportedly declutter the mind by bouncing synchronized sound waves between the brain's two hemispheres, were really onto something.

While such ideas remain speculative, they share strong parallels with reports that iboga delivers a ruthlessly efficient mental spring cleaning. Some report bearing physical witness to their own mental content being re-annexed from one psychological filing cabinet to another, a complete neurological de-fragmentation, the right hemisphere of the brain trading data with the left, during which any excess mental baggage to have outstayed its welcome gets forcefully booted from the premises.

EGO DEATH

Aldous Huxley's *Doors of Perception* may have been penned some time ago. However, it would take the scientific community decades to produce data that seemingly parallels his observations. Either way, his writings remain ranked as one of the most palatable guesstimates concerning the whys and hows of ego death.

On a day-to-day basis, the amount of data transmitted to the brain by the sensory organs is estimated at around 11 million bits per second.[31] If a person were exposed to this entire flood of data, they would likely be consigned to a mental institution shortly thereafter. In order to protect us from this deluge of largely useless information, the average human mind processes a maximum of around 50 bits of information per second.[32] The selection criteria for entry is simple: Is this information practically useful to our survival?

Aldous Huxley termed this neurological function the "reducing valve."[33] As powerful psychedelics begin to take hold, the areas of the brain that usually limit this data stream begin to cease. Eventually, the reducing valve concedes, the floodgates open, and the data stream becomes a tsunami. According to Huxley, this leaves the individual exposed to the entire sum total of their own mind. Huxley termed this "the mind at large." He described this experience as the *"closest a finite mind can ever come to perceiving everything that is happening everywhere in the universe."*[34]

Faced with such profound sensory and perceptual overload,

one's belief in 'separation,' or any association with mind, body, and intellect (the ego) doesn't stand a chance. As Carl Jung notes, any confrontation with such raw power is *"always a defeat for the ego."*[35]

Six decades after Huxley wrote *The Doors of Perception*, the scientific community would produce findings that seem to corroborate his reflections. Robin Carhart-Harris is the head of the Psychedelic Research Group at Imperial College. He is also the first person legally permitted to administer psychedelics since the UK passed the Misuse of Drugs Act in 1971.[36]

In 2009, Carhart-Harris injected a colleague with psilocybin and placed him in an MRI scanner to retrieve data on how the compound affects the brain. Beforehand, his working hypothesis was that the emotion centers of the subject's brain would undergo a sharp increase in activity. In contrast, Carhart-Harris discovered a decrease in blood flow to the brain, and in turn, a decrease in brain activity, with the sharpest drop off occurring in the *default mode network* (DMN).[37]

The true nature of the DMN remains speculative. However, scientists suspect it to be the link between the cerebral cortex and far more ancient parts of the brain associated with memory and emotion. It's also suspected that like the 'reducing valve,' the DMN acts as a kind of neurological filtration system. Marcus Raichle, a neurologist at Washington University, wrote:

> "the DMN acts as an uber-conductor to ensure that the cacophony of competing signals from one system does not interfere with those from another."[38]

Essentially, the DMN's role is to prevent the mental chaff from polluting the wheat, or as Michael Pollan puts it, *"to keep order in a system so complex it might otherwise descend into the anarchy of mental illness."* [39]

It's believed that the DMN plays a lead role in advanced, uniquely human mental processes such as self-reflection, empathy, mental time travel both forward and backward, and essentially, one's sense of self, AKA the 'ego.'[40]

If ever there was a science-backed candidate for Huxley's reducing valve, the DMN would be it. In reference to psychedelics' effect on the DMN, Michael Pollan writes:

> "By quieting the default mode network, these compounds can loosen the ego's grip on the machinery of the mind."[41]

Carhart-Harris's early findings indicated that as the psychedelic-induced drop-off in DMN activity increased, the subject's sense of self decreased.[42] As their ego melted, so did their day-to-day barriers between subject and object and between themselves and the world around them.[43]

This description, of everything merging into one, is often recalled by those who have undergone an iboga journey. Although some neuroscientists may object, descriptions include a feeling of deep oneness with the universe, or God, or Tao. The list goes on.

MEMORY RECOLLECTION

Sigmund Freud's prolific curiosity into the darkest recesses of the human mind, combined with his rapacious appetite for cocaine, may have marked him as an ideal candidate for an iboga experience. Despite some questionable life choices, Freud formulated several theories that went on to become the foundation of psychotherapeutic practices still in use over a century later.

One such theory involved using hypnosis to unearth forgotten childhood memories that continued to cause dysfunction well into the patient's adult lives. Freud believed that transposing these memories from the subconscious to the conscious mind allowed patients to identify, explore and confront their trauma at its source. According to Freud, this allowed patients the opportunity to reframe these memories more positively, thus clearing a path towards mental well-being.

In the century since Freud began using this approach, regression therapy has been criticized over cases in which subjects recalled memories later proven false. Nowadays, academic research supporting the efficacy of this method is both limited and controversial. Nevertheless, iboga is known to provoke similar experiences in subjects seeking to heal past trauma. Many subjects vividly recall witnessing a visual rerun of long past episodes, in which every detail, including how the event made them feel, is displayed in a detached, subjective manner.

Freud-related questions as to whether the memories displayed by iboga are real or not are (in addition to being a false comparison) outside the scope of this book. The sheer volume of reports claiming the iboga-induced resurfacing of such memories served as a powerful and positive means of mental liberation should speak for themselves.

ENTITIES

The suggestion that Charles Dickens was a fan of iboga-fueled escapades is highly doubtful. Nevertheless, he inadvertently created a fitting example of a character who undergoes a similar experience. In *A Christmas Carol*, the main protagonist, Ebenezer Scrooge, is initially portrayed as a cold-hearted, misanthropic miser who cares more about his bank balance than the plight of the poverty-stricken local townsfolk. Pleas and insults from his downtrodden neighbors serve only to entrench the character's mean streak and galvanize his capacity for selfishness. One night, a string of supernatural entities shows Scrooge his past, present, and potential future. He is then reborn a paragon of virtue and sets busily about trying to right past wrongs and share his wealth.

Why was a visit to an alternate reality with a supernatural being, to encounter a crystal clear, immersive reflection of his character the only thing able to make Scrooge see the error of his ways? Could it be because the only real teacher, the only thing capable of instilling true knowledge and unshakable, immutable wisdom, is experience?

Subjects frequently report encounters with sentient beings or entities, who appear utterly bizarre in both form and function. In Heaven and Hell, Aldous Huxley observes:

> "Like the giraffe and the duck-billed platypus, the creatures inhabiting these remoter regions of the mind are exceedingly improbable. Nevertheless, they exist, they are facts of observation; and as such, they cannot be ignored by anyone who is honestly trying to understand the world in which he lives."[44]

Although Huxley's observations were based on his experiences with mescaline, the same comparison applies to the iboga journey, particularly in the early stages. As the iboga experience progresses, these beings tend to take on a more benevolent disposition and become far more lucid in both form and function. Following these encounters, users may be left convinced they communicated with some form of higher wisdom or power. Labels include God, their own soul or true self, guiding entities, or the spirit of iboga. Regardless of their essence or nature, they seem to share a common trait; a willingness to transmit to the subject vital lessons and authoritative wisdom on how best to self-actualize and thereby experience a life free of unnecessary suffering.

During the latter stages of the journey, such beings can appear with remarkable clarity. Consequently, many return convinced that these beings were absolutely real. Whether such beings exist autonomously and would continue to exist outside one's personal encounter is a question as old as humankind's capacity for abstract thinking.

TAPPING THE SOURCE

Imagine being with a friend, and asking "why is it that my relationships fail," or "why am I in a constant state of existential despair?" Imagine they answered, "Well, have you thought about being less self-centered," or "have you ever considered your means of employment to be of little help to the greater good of society?" In some cases, the response may involve a vague acknowledgment that your friend is correct, followed by an awkward change of topic. In more severe cases, your friend's perceived audacity may cop them a scathing rebuke. After all, why would the agoraphobic demons that fester in the darkest corners of a person's psyche welcome a spotlight being shone upon them?

Now imagine a rather different scenario. You ask the friend the same questions. In this instance, your friend is a seasoned author who understands a guiding principle of any professional writer - 'show, don't tell.' He also just happens to be a dimension-hopping magician. Instead of responding with placatory small talk, he clicks his fingers. A nanosecond later, you find yourself magically immersed in a lucid, real-time role-playing experience. In order to resolve your questions, your friend introduces you to a source of loving, infinite intelligence, as weird as it is wise. So poignant, so undeniably true are the bombshell epiphanies that flow from these celestial transmissions, they forever change the way you approach life. Upon returning, you find yourself gifted with a brand new, far more effective set of psychological maps and tools to draw from. Consequently, the mindset with which you approach previously insurmountable obstacles surrounding relationships, existential angst, and much more is forever changed.

Volumes of user testimonies exist to support claims iboga delivers scarily clear-cut answers to the kind of deep, complex questions that decades of soul searching and even therapy has failed to resolve. In recalling their experience, many have confirmed this phenomenon to be not only true, but that the information imparted served as the foundation for huge changes in the way they live, and acted as an editor to the stories they tell themselves about themselves.

In addition to internal questions regarding ourselves and our behavior, iboga can provide answers to the type of external, macrocosmic inquiries that shall be explored in greater detail shortly.

Although, the maxim "ask and thy shall receive" is largely applicable, it's not quite that simple. In order to maximize this opportunity, it's advised beforehand that the subject thinks deeply about what they wish to receive from the experience. Consequently, both the question and how best to phrase it will become clear.

Access to this transformative wisdom is why iboga remains so highly revered as a divination tool by Bwiti culture. Bwiti shamans believe iboga facilitates direct dialogue with your higher self or soul. They believe the human soul possesses infinite knowledge, which it communicates via various channels. Interestingly, subjects often claim the information came not from an external source but was unearthed from a place within themselves, long since buried. As such, some claim not to be learning but "remembering," or as "a recollection of one's infinite true nature."

Iboga is eaten by the Bwiti for the purpose of seeing, knowing, and to commune with the powers that lie hidden in it and known through it. From the Bwiti perspective, to consume iboga for the purpose of casual, meaningless inquiry is a form of dishonesty.[45] As such, requesting lottery numbers, how to gain a leg up on a rival, or similar inquiries may at best be met with silence. Or, at worst, a cosmic clip around the ear in whichever form iboga deems suitably effective.

That said, questions rooted in altruism, benevolence, and a desire to improve oneself and the world around them are often met with the informational tools necessary to achieve a competitive advantage. This can manifest via improvements in relationships, aptitude, motivation, sense of purpose, and much more. And so, while requesting the location of buried cash is a fool's errand, asking "what behavioral patterns continue to sabotage my capacity to care for myself, my family, my friends, and others" may just unearth another far more valuable treasure buried deep within you.

Prior to an ayahuasca ceremony, a shaman may insist the subject 'set their intent' and meditate on it before they drink. Although an overall intention setting is also strongly recommended, it's a good idea to enter an iboga ceremony with a written list of questions drawn up beforehand. This provides a reference point for subjects to fall back on during the question-and-answer part of their journey.

As mentioned, the best questions to ask are those, which, if answered, will act as a powerful and constructive positive force. The nature of one's inquiries is an entirely subjective affair. However, the following questions are offered as a rough guide to the kind of inquiries iboga seems happiest to answer.

- What is the root cause of my addictive behavior?
- How can I learn to respect myself more?
- How can I create a life of health, happiness, and abundance?
- How can I forgive those who have hurt me?
- What scares me, and how do I overcome my fears?
- What do I do to sabotage myself, and how can I stop?
- How can I free myself from patterns of insecurity/inferiority/jealousy etc.?
- What diet suits me best?
- To what personal and professional roles am I best suited?
- What is my life's purpose?
- What can I do to embark on my true path, begin to create my destiny, and actualize my best self?
- How does the universe work, and what is humankind's role within it?
- What is the history and potential future of planet earth?

Labels attached to the source of this knowledge include the higher self, human soul, Dr. Iboga, even God. Then, there's Robin Carhart-Harris, who pays short shrift to the idea that these insights are in any way supernatural. Instead, he suggests they are a property of the human brain.

The logic goes something like this: In order to formulate the answer to a question, the brain begins by rounding up the varied items of relevant data at our disposal (often what we have heard, seen, read, or otherwise absorbed). More often than not, the scale used to weigh these data points' validity is tipped heavily in one direction by our biases and desires. Consequently, the answers it usually prints out are entirely subjective. Robin Carhart-Harris suspects the reason psychedelic insights are so often held to be objectively true may be due to a loss of any clear distinction between subject and object.[46] When the capacity for subjectivity (the ego) breaks down, taking with it the background noise of opposing inner voices and personal bias, all that's left is the untarnished object, which looks, feels, and sounds emphatically like an objective, bias-free, fact-of-the-matter answer to a question.

In truth, we are a long way from understanding how iboga does this. Regardless, iboga doesn't pull any punches when it comes to letting you know exactly what's up. Although such revelations are delivered with tough love, this messenger has an important task and knows precisely how to get the job done. Consequently, some people find the content of such an exchange to be painstakingly honest. Deceit, jealousy, intolerance, superficiality, vanity, greed, arrogance, and any other deeply rooted, damaging character traits are paraded into the light and exposed for what they are; towering hurdles standing on the path between you and whom you wish to become. In this regard, the only major difference between psychotherapy and an iboga journey may be the speed at which such conclusions are reached. While the former may take years, the latter takes seconds.

NEAR-DEATH EXPERIENCE

Although few have experienced it directly, we've all heard the stories of those who have died on the operating table, only to return moments later with mind-boggling tales of otherworldly adventures. Even more incredible is that different NDE subjects report a range of uncannily common elements. These include subjective knowledge that one has died, a feeling of serenity and well-being, leaving the body, being drawn to a light at the end of a tunnel, life reviews, encounters with other beings, and an eventual return to life, all the while feeling a tremendous sense of peace, security, and warmth.

In the hallways of academic psychedelia, the near-death experience (NDE) ranks high on the list of "peak experiences." Such claims are nothing new, and the NDE often constitutes the very essence of shamanic practices from Africa to Mesoamerica and beyond. Like the Bwiti, the shamanic cultures of South America also consider the NDE, and subsequent rebirth, to be the ultimate shamanic initiation.

So moved are those who return, it often becomes the foundation for permanent transformation. Many claim the experience removed any doubt that physical death is either frightening or marks the end of consciousness, thus providing a fresh and far more optimistic outlook on existence.

Medical, scientific, religious, and psychedelic literature is swamped with countless reports from individuals who recall the near-death experience with unshakable confidence and clarity. Obviously, this is all open to debate. The very fact that an explanation of how death feels is made by people who didn't die means nothing can be ascertained with any true certainty. Still, most people who undergo an NDE laud it as one of the most, if not the most, profound experiences of their lives. Although mainstream medical researchers would concur that something very mysterious is undoubtedly taking place, they may disagree on the origins of such experiences.

Given the NDE is both powerful and vivid, it's easy to understand why returnees ascribe a metaphysical nature to the experience. After all, what biological function would such an encounter otherwise serve? What evolutionary purpose would the human genes have for constructing a false yet elaborate virtual reality created solely to trick people into believing that death is pleasurable?

The most popular explanation (particularly among those who have experienced it) is that it is exactly what it appears: an encounter with what awaits us following the death of our physical body. If proven correct, then we would have evidence that death is a mere stepping stone through which our soul, mind, essence, or consciousness passes to an immaterial plane of being.

Then, there are the scientific attempts to account for such experiences. Despite a lack of conclusive proof, such findings allude to complicated neuronal mechanisms triggered during a perceived or real life-threatening event. Although scientific explanations for the NDE vary, they all follow the same basic blueprint and identify the NDE as a natural neurological response to the tsunami of endorphins that swamp the brain when the "game over" signal begins to flash.

This alternative explanation may represent a far bleaker prospect than many would wish to contemplate; that this warm, cozy drift into death is indeed little more than a colossal cosmic prank, the ultimate "bait and switch" concocted by the genes in order to hoodwink us into believing that our post-mortem existence surpasses our wildest imaginings, thus diverting our attention from the search for physical immortality. After all, what possible benefit do the genes have to gain from the human search for immortality? Why would our evolutionary hardware conspire to produce a population of immortals, busily squandering natural resources at the expense of future generations and thus threatening the survival of the entire species? According to such logic, the NDE may indeed serve a vital purpose; to return and misinform the species that death is merely a footbridge to an alternate reality in which the loving embrace of one's dearly departed awaits. False advertising at its finest and darkest.

This idea that the NDE is little more than a highly sophisticated ontological mousetrap fails to account for certain factors that continue to baffle neuroscientists. Namely, cases in which patients have returned after being pronounced brain dead. Furthermore, it stops short of explaining claims that the episode bestowed a multitude of psychological benefits on those who return.

Answers regarding the source, meaning, and purpose of the NDE will obviously remain speculative until one's demise. Nevertheless, it has been shown to catalyze dramatic, lasting personal change. Usually, subjects return asking the same question: What would they do with their life if given another chance? Having lost their fear of death, they have lost their fear of life, and fear of taking chances. This massively broadened perspective becomes the foundation of a new existential vision, a chance to view the world with fresh eyes and approach personal issues from a different angle. Claims include a diminished fear of death, less focus on materialism, increased strength, tolerance, confidence, calm, and clarity, and, a desire to live regret-free with increased attention on the present moment.

These near-death-induced aspects of personal optimization correlate closely with the desired outcome of a Bwiti initiation ceremony. The death-rebirth journey and the consequent inner changes bestowed on the initiate lies at the very heart of Bwiti practice and other forms of shamanism. To them, experiencing this journey to the afterlife is about coming to terms with death.[47]

CONTACT WITH ANCESTORS

The word "Bwiti" roughly translates to mean "dead," "deceased," or "ancestor." According to Bwiti, no one can become a Bwiti member until they have seen Bwiti for themselves. And, the one-and-only way to see Bwiti is to eat iboga.

Traditional African spiritual beliefs are highly diverse, and many incorporate ancestor worship into their practice. Bwiti is one such religion. The difference, however, is that a Bwiti initiation involves getting up close and personal with the deceased and communicating directly. This lucid, face-to-face contact is a key element of the initiation ceremony and is believed to facilitate strong personal relationships with one's ancestors. During these meetings, initiates often report insights into the common African origins of all initiates, regardless of skin color. Although speculative, such ancestral liaisons may correlate closely with NDE reports, psychedelic or otherwise. Like NDE reports, the idea of meeting dead ancestors would burden scientific researchers with one more reason to keep scratching their heads. As Terrence Mckenna points out:

> "The existence of an ecology of souls is not something that science can be expected to grapple with and emerge with its own premises intact."[48]

TIME TRAVEL

More about this later.

5

THE PSYCHOTHERAPIST

In September 2003, Daniel Pinchbeck, author of *Breaking Open the Head*, wrote an article for the UK's Guardian newspaper about his iboga ceremony and Bwiti initiation process. *"Ten Years of Therapy in One Night,"* read the article's headline.[49] Since then, this quote has been cut, pasted, rehashed, and become common parlance in iboga-related discussions. The reason is simple; because many subjects have a similar experience. However, in the wider psychedelic community, reports of similar-sounding therapeutic benefits are nothing new. So, from a psychotherapy standpoint, what makes iboga different?

THE ALTERED STATE EXPRESS LANE

One thing that binds therapy, meditation, yoga, and any other means of inner exploration, is that results require time, discipline, commitment, and patience. Exploration of one's subconscious, even with the aid of a therapist, can be a complex and challenging undertaking.

Then, there's psychedelics, which are immediate, overwhelming, and providing they're well-sourced, guaranteed. In the place of patience and commitment, one can make do with a few dollars and the phone number of a reliable dealer. *"Transcendence on demand"* is how writer Oliver Sacks describes this dividing line.[50]

It is precisely this shortcut to an experience that can and may blow one's mind that sets psychedelics apart from any other means of internal inquiry. Despite piles of research attesting to their potential value, this is also why some in the professional therapy community remain unconvinced and even suspicious as to whether these compounds' benefits justify the potential risks.

In the Foreword to *LSD: My Problem Child,* LSD inventor Albert Hofman explicitly cautions that the deliberate provocation of mystical experience carries potential psychological and spiritual dangers, and warns their misuse carries the same capacity to harm as it does to heal.[51] Psychedelics can be a double-edged sword. Where angels dwell, so, too, may demons.[52] Where some discover transcendent bliss, others encounter abject terror. Such occurrences are extreme, and their citation may appear alarmist. It is not the author's intention to cast doubt over the excellent work being done by universities and therapy centers. However, such cases highlight why several respected psychoanalysts remain unconvinced. One such skeptic was Carl Jung.

Jung's uncertainty prompted him to disavow the psychedelic experience. *"I am profoundly mistrustful of the pure gifts of the Gods,"* he wrote in a letter to Victor White, an English Dominican priest and theologian. *"You pay very dearly for them."*[53]

Jung, the undisputed heavyweight champion of transpersonal psychology, didn't say such things lightly. He believed psychedelic exploration revealed more unconscious content than the human mind could healthily integrate or absorb. Considering Jung was referring to compounds common to the time, particularly mescaline, and that his opinions reflect an era long before modern research began, he may have raised a point worth considering.[54]

Jung believed the ideal therapeutic setting to be the dream state, which is arguably a smaller scale version of ego death. The dream state thought Jung, relaxed the subject, pacified the ego, and allowed access and insight into the mind. Here, the dreamer would encounter the 'archetype' imagery Jung believed lay at the root of every human psyche. According to Jung, dream analysis allowed progress to proceed at a safer, more gradual pace. He believed the clear, chronological visionary data that emerged from the dream state to be far more reliable than the swirling, unintelligible hallucinations reported by users of psychedelics.

What then, would Jung have made of an obscure African root, thought to activate the brain as if its owner were asleep but were actually wide awake? Upon learning of a plant capable of inducing visions strikingly similar to that of the dream state, would Jung's views on psychedelic therapy have changed?

MOVIES ON DEMAND

There's nothing swirling or unintelligible about the content reported in the visionary stages of an iboga journey. The factor that places iboga in a visionary category of its own, beyond LSD, psilocybin, even DMT, is the unambiguous, easily-interpreted, easily-remembered manner in which this content often reveals itself; via visions of startling clarity.

Imagine turning on Netflix. Instead of the usual menu of movies and shows, you're shown a somewhat different list of viewing options. In one corner, there's the time when you rode your first bicycle, or the first day of preschool, along with countless more options to select from. Sure, you can return to riding your bike or receiving that long-awaited toy at a child-hood birthday party. But, let's suppose your quest is to unearth the root cause of your addictive tendencies. Your healing intent has been set, and you have the spirit of iboga issuing instructions on where to left-click your mental mouse. Hey Presto! It seems you're headed to a birthday party after all.

Faster than the speed of thought, you touch down in a scenario long since buried in your subconscious. As the rerun of this traumatic episode unfolds, you see how the void that later became a vacuum for substance abuse, gambling, alcohol, or other damaging life-choices was created. As the layers of psychological scar tissue are torn away, the mental anguish you'd expect from such a raw experience is instead replaced by a feeling of detached, objective, almost academic curiosity. Almost as if you are playing the role of both researcher and research subject.

This is only one of the countless examples among the infinitely varied visions iboga may project. If we assume these visions to be accurate (not all do) and that they provide the conscious subject an opportunity to visualize key events from their past, would iboga's value as a psychotherapeutic tool not take on a whole new meaning? After all, many therapists regard this material as the holy grail of psychotherapeutic pursuit and spend years, even decades, attempting to provoke a similar state. Furthermore, it's not just the visions that help resolve psychological problems but the overall 'transcendental experience,' or to use astronaut terminology; the "overview effect."

THE DREAM MAKER

In the 1960s, Claudio Naranjo, a Chilean psychiatrist, conducted studies into ibogaines psychotherapeutic potential. He concluded that ibogaine gives rise to an oneirogenic state of consciousness. The word "oneirogen" is a portmanteau of the Greek words óneiros meaning dream, and *gen* meaning to create. Ibogaine, said Naranjo, is a *dream creator*. Some years later, data from animal studies would lend weight to the idea that ibogaine does indeed seem to recreate neurological effects consistent with deep REM sleep.[55]

Like Jung, Claudio Naranjo believed that this dream-like state of consciousness allowed access to a rich arsenal of therapeutic material to draw from. Unlike Jung, who probably had to navigate subjects' sleep cycles and fuzzy half-memories, Naranjo had access to a powerful compound believed to induce "guided day-dreams" and visions they could articulate with clarity.[56]

In 1969, one year before ibogaine research was outlawed, Naranjo became one of the only individuals ever legally permitted to administer ibogaine in a psychotherapeutic setting. Interestingly, Naranjo's investigations led him to believe that the ibogaine-induced visions were not crystal-clear memories of actual external events but rather inner events or fantasies.[57] After overseeing many ibogaine-assisted therapy sessions, Naranjo described ibogaine as a compound that brought out the psyche's instinctual side. He concluded its power lies in its ability to provoke vivid, archetype-rich visual encounters, which could be easily communicated from patient to healer.[58]

During a Bwiti ceremony, the waking consciousness of the subject, and the ability to communicate their visions to the healer, both during and after, is considered a crucial component of healing. During a ceremony, Bwiti healers maintain verbal communication with the subject, constantly inquiring about the nature of their visions. The only visions considered to be of value are those that are remembered and thus able to be committed to long-term memory. To an experienced psychotherapist, these 'pseudo-memories' contain invaluable insights into the subject's psychological plight and a solid foundation from which to enact real-world personal transformation.[59, 60]

In The Healing Journey, Naranjo writes:

> "LSD is like a look out of a window into the open; ibogaine is more like an occasion to destroy the old building and make room for a new one. It is more of a 'work drug' in the sense of facilitating an analytic process on the unconscious obstacles to life."[61]

In the half-century since Naranjo published his findings, data from observational research trials has concurred that ibogaine is eminently capable of helping people to overcome depression, obsessive-compulsive disorder, anxiety, and other psychological hurdles.[62] Its actions have been reported to remain ongoing long after ibogaine's immediate effects subside, serving as a permanent game-changer for those involved.[63]

THE COUNTER ARGUMENT

Some may object that the material outlined thus far is overly optimistic and fails to account for documented psychological pitfalls associated with iboga and other compounds. Such arguments are based on a tiny number of example cases.

The truth is that the vast majority of iboga subjects return with glowing reports of the plants' psychotherapeutic benefits. In contrast, there have been instances where things didn't turn out so well. These rare cases lend weight to the idea that some subjects should be green-lighted by therapy professionals prior to their journey.

What follows is not presented to discourage readers from working with iboga, but because to tell anything less than the full story would be negligent.

Too Much Information

Echoing Carl Jung's concerns, iboga has been criticized as a shortcut that circumvents the formal, delicately-paced psycho-therapeutic process. Some argue that the speed at which sub-conscious content emerges may be too rapid for some patients to absorb and later integrate, particularly in patients with a history of repeated trauma.

Similarly, some therapists argue that the sheer volume of mental content bursting out from the psyche's repressed corners is just too much. They say it may trigger natural psychological defense mechanisms that exist to stem the flow of pain-inducing material, creating a bottleneck of emotional traffic along all the wrong neurological roads and pathways. In a few cases, it's been claimed that the resultant inner turmoil may give rise to delusional or neurotic beliefs that persist after the journey ends.

Comfortably Numb

Another criticism, one that applies specifically to iboga, involves revisiting scenarios that would otherwise cause pain and anguish, with objectivity and detachment. This may sound like a comforting way to approach such material. In contrast, it could be argued that such detachment forgoes any emotional connection with the event, thus depriving the subject of the crucial cathartic release necessary to achieve solid therapeutic results. Similarly, this 'detachment' may allow the patient to emerge from the experience with their ego unscathed, which some say makes the process insufficient for catalyzing lasting change.

Iboga has been erroneously labeled a "magic bullet" in the treatment of addictions. It would be equally false to apply this moniker in a psychotherapeutic context. Iboga is eminently capable of planting the psychological seeds necessary to move forward. However, seeds need watering. In the absence of any efforts from the stranded car owner, the wrench and jack aren't going to change a blown tire. Iboga appears to work in the same manner; as a tool, which can be an effective means to get you back on the road if used correctly and conscientiously. Just because iboga can provide the perfect springboard from which to plunge into a new mode of being doesn't mean it can push you off the edge. However, it can certainly make the edge appear far less threatening, the jump more exhilarating, and the water below warmer, more inviting, and free of the malevolent sea monsters that once lurked in its murky depths.

Arguments for and against the true potential of iboga's therapeutic value will likely remain ongoing. Despite differences, there are certain points that all competent psychedelic therapists agree on. First, anyone suffering from severe mental health issues should consider whether this is the right choice for them. Finally, iboga is more than capable of standalone results. However, just as Bwiti initiates have their visions interpreted by Bwiti shamans, a trained psychotherapist may be better able to paint a clearer picture and expedite the integration process.

II

IBOGAINE:
THE ADDICTION INTERRUPTER

6

WHAT IBOGAINE CAN DO

Imagine a magic mirror. Instead of displaying one's physical exterior, it reflects back a surreal image of one's deep emotions, emotional processes, motivations, memories, experiences, and stored traumas. Stranger still, it lays bare how these components interconnect to shape one's personality, behavior, actions, and reactions. If such a mirror were invented, the entire psychotherapy field would wake up jobless the next morning.

"Introspection," meaning the process of taking a deep inward look at oneself, can be a daunting, if not impossible challenge to undertake alone. With ibogaine, you are not alone.

Sometime after ingesting ibogaine, the 'introspective' phase of the journey may begin. Once the ego is tied and gagged, one can storm the undefended walls of the psyche's inner sanctum, where buried memories, both real and archetypal, reside. This revelatory tour of one's subconscious may include big answers to big questions, a reconciliation with the subconscious pain that drives addiction, and access to a more ancient, more meaningful existential narrative through which to empower oneself.

Incredible as this sounds, those familiar with other, better-known psychedelics may reply, "so what?" They may argue that ibogaine's capacity for introspection, epiphanies, and healing sounds no different than that of LSD or psilocybin. They, too, have been shown to help addicts in much the same manner. In many ways, they would be correct.

"My violence, my drug habits, my reckless sexual escapades, my street fights, and car accidents, all that time is over," said Mike Tyson, the human wrecking ball whose ringside and street-level transgressions transformed a story of sporting Godhood into the heavyweight champion of cautionary tales. Fortunately for Tyson, his story wasn't yet complete. *"I won't say it is God, but it was the death of my ego. I felt so naked and afraid because all I ever had was my ego,"* says Tyson.[64]

Tyson's spiritual upheaval and subsequent behavioral U-turn wasn't due to therapy, or an ibogaine journey, or LSD or mushrooms. He was talking about smoking raw toad venom, more commonly known as 5-MEO-DMT.

Like 5-MEO-DMT, ibogaine's ability to unlock realms of consciousness that conventional therapies simply can't touch is a comparatively new discovery, at least in the west. However, LSD and psilocybin's ability to induce ego death, deep reflection, personal transformation, transcendental states, and even the will to break addictions has been recognized for nearly a century. Like ibogaine, they too are eminently capable of driving the subject forward through paralyzing emotional roadblocks. Like ibogaine, they can facilitate a state of enhanced neuroplasticity and reveal the healthy, actualized version of oneself that exists on the other side of social constructions and toxic patterns.

As Benjamin Taub points out, psychedelic treatment for addiction *"is not really about drug use per se, but rather aims at transforming the narratives behind the addiction."*[65] Similarly, Matt Johnson, Ph.D., a psychiatry and behavioral sciences professor at Johns Hopkins University, believes *"addiction is a story we get stuck in"* and that the power of psilocybin and other psychedelics rests in their ability to trigger an experience dramatic enough to *"dope-slap"* people out of their own narratives, reboot their system, and temporarily provide the mental flexibility to flip the perspectives they use to organize reality.[66] By identifying and replacing destructive self-chatter with far healthier inner monologues, classic psychedelics also change the stories you tell yourself about yourself.

So, if other psychedelics are equally capable of transforming these narratives, what makes ibogaine different from ayahuasca, psilocybin, LSD, or toad venom? Is it really so special?

What Makes Iboga(ine) Different?

Suppose ibogaine's capacity to interrupt addiction was limited only to the "psycho-spiritual" journey. In that case, the clear visions notwithstanding, drawing any distinction between ibogaine and other psychedelic compounds could be a challenge. However, the "psycho-spiritual" journey is just one apparatus in ibogaine's arsenal.

For illustrative purposes, let's imagine a person has committed to confronting and battling the cunning, sneaky, well hidden, heavily armed, highly agile demons of addiction. They know full well that these malignant spirits refuse to go down easily. Instead, the prospect of being evicted from their home will prompt them to kick, scream, and lash out violently. This is no journey for the faint-hearted. Fortunately, the traveler may select one of two weapons packages to help them on their crusade.

Weapons Package A:

•   Transport to the demon's home turf.
•   A lie detector to expose the falsity of their words.

- A lens through which to look them in the eye and gain a sense of their true nature.
- The revealing of their true names and the subsequent authority to demand they "Be gone."
- A valuable book, fresh off the press, containing a robust, inspiring personal mythology, custom authored to allow the subject to reclaim their place in the world. Or, alternatively, a book of blank pages that frees them to write the story themselves from scratch.

Weapons Package B:

- All of the above.
- A Magic, inexplicably effective force field capable of deflecting bullets, anesthetizing potential real-world injuries, and repairing the neurological damage sustained during the relationship with these psychic vandals. Demons don't die easily, nor quickly and quietly. Not only do its shielding effects last the length of the fight, but they continue to protect against any desperate, last-ditch parting shots the creatures may hurl as they enter their death throes. As you turn around and walk away, this shield continues to guard your rear.

Which would you choose?

Unlike other psychedelics, ibogaine bonds with the same neuroreceptors as heroin, making it uniquely suited to treating opiate dependency. It is a holistic treatment whose various actions overlap, intersect, and combine to beat opioid addiction along a continuum of interconnected factors. If its status as a uniquely capable psychedelic and true pharmacological miracle hung only upon a few pieces of evidence, the exhibits would be:

1. Ibogaine sidesteps the torments of opiate withdrawal.
2. Ibogaine resets the opioid receptors to a novice state.
3. Ibogaine prolongs the suppression of cravings.

1: Pain Avoidance

Ask most opiate addicts to identify the most dread-inducing aspect of detox, and "the horror of withdrawal symptoms" will likely be the reply. So, when word gets around of a compound mysteriously able to circumvent these otherwise guaranteed tortures, interest is bound to skyrocket.

What limited findings exist allude to serotonin uptake, dopamine blocking, and more. However, ibogaine's capacity to quell any protest from these hungry, opioid-denied receptors, and by extension, replace vomiting, cramping, nausea, hot and cold sweats, goosebumps, and anxiety with a relatively painless detox experience, remains an unresolved question.

2: Beginner's Mind

If abused for long enough, opioids eventually alter the structure and action of specific neurotransmitters and receptor sites in the brain. They essentially cause brain damage.

It is believed that ibogaine reverses this drug-inflicted deterioration and returns the brain's opioid receptors to a novice state.[67] With one's neurological slate wiped clean, it offers the cognitive freedom to replace old behavioral patterns with new ones. If these drug-swamped receptor sites are the malware-ridden computer, then ibogaine would be the state-of-the-art virus eliminator, able to restore the hard drive's speed and efficiency back to full operational capacity.

3: The Gift that Keeps Giving

Ibogaine's power to reduce or eliminate cravings during the withdrawal phase is without question. However, long after ibogaine's immediate effects have subsided, physical cravings may remain a fraction of what they once were. Noribogaine, the long-lasting, residual metabolite of ibogaine, is the compound believed responsible for these effects.[68]

It has been hypothesized that ibogaine's capacity to mimic REM sleep actuates a period of highly increased neuroplasticity, during which stubborn thought patterns and pathological triggers to seek refuge in harmful substances can be reprocessed.[69, 70] This period may range anywhere from a week to much longer and represents a golden opportunity to rediscover how to live a functional life, free from compulsions that were inescapable only days previously. It's a time when patterns such as healthy eating, sleeping, exercise, or artistic pursuits come easy. This "window of opportunity" for ongoing self-empowerment should be seized with gusto.

WHO IS IBOGAINE FOR?

It's been written that *"change happens when the pain of staying the same is greater than the pain of change."* For many whose addictions have wrought havoc on their work, relationships, and physical health, there may come a time when the existential weight "of staying the same" is just too heavy to bear. A common epithet for this dark place is "rock bottom."

SICK AND TIRED OF BEING SICK AND TIRED

Many who have received the life-changing freedom ibogaine can offer have spent time at rock bottom. In the face of a seemingly inescapable cascade of serious problems, they finally declared "enough." Instead of the flight option, they opted to fight with ibogaine. Afterward, they understood the idea of the universe "having your back" was more than an abstract platitude, but manifest here on earth, in the form of a mysterious, powerful molecule from the African Jungle.

To take from this the idea that "rock bottom" is an ideal place for anyone to be, or that ibogaine's benefits extend only to those who dwell there would be a mistake. However, when it comes to lighting a fire below someone's rear end, the sheer power of hitting the bricks, or at least identifying the collision course and slamming the brakes, can be unparalleled.

Ibogaine can be helpful at varying levels of dependency and will meet an individual at whichever stage of their journey they are on. However, it works best with those resolute in their determination to break the addictive cycle and terminate their dependence on harmful substances.

Crucially, one must understand the dividing line between ibogaine's limitations and personal responsibility. The biochemical mechanisms of ibogaine can lessen withdrawal symptoms, act as an introspective mirror, blast wash the neurological pathways, and reduce long-term cravings. But these effects will eventually wear off. Similarly, the post-treatment spark of inspiration, gratitude, and enhanced neuroplasticity, a period in which many correctly believe anything is possible, will dwindle over time.

It has been repeatedly stated that ibogaine is not a "magic bullet." However, recall that ibogaine pioneer Howard Lotsof described iboga as *a laser-guided smart missile for trauma.*

Much like the proverbial guided missile, if the bullet in question is subject to careful, intent-driven tweaks in trajectory, then maybe the "magic bullet" metaphor may have more to it.

Ibogaine's magic has limits. However, those limits are much less about ibogaine and much more about the individual. Essentially, ibogaine's power as an addiction interrupter parallels one's individual will. If an addicted individual does not wish to change, then ibogaine cannot help them. However, if their desire to change exceeds whatever forces have been holding them back, ibogaine could be the perfect start.

7

WHAT IBOGAINE CAN'T DO

Let us imagine someone who recently finished an ibogaine treatment. Withdrawal was undergone, physical cravings have been effectively abolished, and the root causes of their addictive tendencies have been reflected back at them. Congratulations. Now what?

The answer depends on a range of interdependent factors, most of which can be surmised with one word: "Intent." Like a runner fresh off the starting blocks, now the real work begins. Those who fail to understand that ibogaine's power, although remarkable, is subject to limitations and cannot alter a person's free will may well be doomed to relapse.

For those who think ibogaine treatment involves jetting off to a tropical location, tripping out for a while, and then returning home with zero to worry about, then ibogaine is unlikely to fulfill its potential. At best, they may return home tanned and a little healthier, followed by an eventual return to substance abuse. At worst, a person's return to substance abuse may be immediate, leaving them incorrectly and dangerously convinced that if the most powerful anti-addiction package on the planet failed them, then there's no hope left.

Likewise, anyone pressured or emotionally blackmailed into seeking ibogaine may be destined to relapse. It's a question of personal choice. To quit an addiction, the person must want to quit. While ibogaine may banish cravings, it has no power to eradicate free will. A fitting, albeit extreme example, may be the tale of the addict chained to a radiator by a desperate loved one at their wit's end. True or not, this story of a well-meaning, outside attempt at salvation fails to account for one crucial component of beating addiction: The addict did not voluntarily choose to be there. If the mental chains are still strong, then unless you intend to shackle them for life, physical chains may be useless.

Few would agree that the addict in this hypothetical scenario deserves to be chained to a radiator. For argument's sake, let's say their current status (chained and unable to free themselves) is an adverse consequence of their addiction. Then, let us consider the dictionary definition of addiction as *"the compulsion to engage in behaviors despite negative consequences."*

What this means is that stubborn resistance, even in the face of pain, is all too often an inherent component of the condition. Such gritty, masochistic defiance may be noble on the battlefield. However, when the battlefield is inside and against oneself, it may be an entirely different story. Granted, knowing one's enemy, or in this context, acquiring a cognitive grasp of the underlying elements of one's addiction, may be a crucial aspect of victory. But does such insight automatically spark lasting behavioral changes?

Psychologist and psychedelic researcher, Ralph Metzner, stated: *"having an insight is not the same as being able to apply that insight."* [71] Similarly, psychiatrist Roger Walsh asks whether altered states lead to altered traits?[72] Can the insights imparted during the ibogaine journey become cemented in the psyche rather than remain just a fleeting experience? The answer is sometimes, but not always. Even after staying clean for years, the desire to re-engage one's long-lost nemesis may remain strong.

Ibogaine is an alarm clock, which affords the owner equal opportunity to hit snooze as it does to rise and apply the teachings of their experience toward building a life. The kind of life that feels better and provides more meaning than that offered by drugs or booze coursing through one's veins.

Once again, the dividing factors between those who manage to remain opiate or alcohol-free often come down to one thing; disciplined personal choice, especially in the face of temptation. Until something more powerful appears, ibogaine will remain the most effective addiction interrupter we know of. Yet still, it is a catalyst, not a cure. It is a means to a start. If used conscientiously and integrated into a broader game plan for resuming control of one's life, it may well be the best start.

8

CHOOSING A PROVIDER

Commitment to ibogaine treatment for addiction is no small thing. It is a hard-hitting medical procedure to be embarked upon with open eyes. After committing, it's time to begin with practical matters, the first being where and with whom to receive treatment. At this point, treatment seekers must hold onto the fire in their belly that prompted them to finally declare "enough is enough." Of equal importance is not to allow this enthusiasm to cloud one's judgment, resulting in a poor choice of ibogaine provider.

There are many complex factors in play before, during, and after an ibogaine addiction treatment. Although mishaps remain rare, it's widely agreed they occur because of someone's failure to do their homework. Decades ago, in the absence of relevant study material, this may have been a loosely valid excuse. Times have changed. Treatment seekers are advised to read the literature, recognize the red flags, and stay alert for cowboys and charlatans.

In contrast, there's an increasing number of professional, caring providers doing incredible work. If approached smartly, sorting between the two is not difficult. This is the time to begin separating the good, the bad, and the ugly, which will reap huge rewards if performed objectively and patiently.

The first stop for most is the internet. Here, one can find a range of providers explaining why you should put your money where their mouth is. Unfortunately, the SEO algorithms only measure words and not the caliber of whoever authored them. The fact that nobody in the business is likely to advertise their own shortcomings can make treatment provider websites a confusing place to separate charlatans from legitimate providers.

Many of these locations will offer reiki, stone ceremonies, massages, 5-star organic cuisine, horse-riding, surfing, and swanky digs. There's nothing wrong with this. If anything, a post-treatment taste of the good life may be a good way to remind oneself that the world isn't such a dark place after all. But if luxury amenities are the main draw, a rethink might be in order.

Take the online reviews with a grain of salt. They can be a fair indicator of competence but may also be inaccurate, biased, or written by business owners or friends. Beware of newly established centers with a suspiciously long list of positive reviews. In contrast, treatment centers with a long history of reviews have obviously been in business longer. Even though the odd lousy review may appear, at least it's an indicator that these centers have been in business for an extended period. These centers may have experienced problems with people who misrepresented themselves during the screening process or dismissed the importance of aftercare. Despite the provider's best efforts, some individuals may leave unhappy and write a negative review. Competitors seeking to negatively impact a center's reputation may also do the same.

What To Look For in a Provider

Transparency

Any well-run treatment center's website should highlight everything they offer, down to the last detail. This includes staff names, resumes, training, experience, and academic credentials.

Remember that transparency flows two ways. Providers committed to helping you safely achieve your goals will require every relevant piece of information about your addiction. They should know which questions to ask to gauge their ability to help you. This is the time to be open. They aren't the police. They're the people trying to help you turn your life around. In addition to being dangerous, neglecting to inform them of your habits or your pre or post-treatment plans will make it difficult for them to tailor the safe treatment you need and attain the results you seek. Help them help you.

Medical Experience

Ibogaine-assisted detoxification from drugs is a heavyweight medical intervention. Getting off drugs can be a risky affair, not made any safer if your ibogaine is administered by a novice practitioner unable to distinguish between sherbet and smack.

This is where research will reward you. Interview the provider and quiz them on their qualifications. Reputable providers will likely do the same and ask questions you'd maybe neither thought of nor knew could be an issue. Their skill level should quickly become evident. The same applies to bad providers.

Questions may include the following:

• Do they have experience in recognizing pre or post-treatment physical withdrawal symptoms?

- Are they equipped with the knowledge of timing and dosing that such a condition demands?
- Are they experienced in recognizing withdrawal symptoms during treatment, and how to counteract them?
- Can they spot increased sensitivity to ibogaine and decide to decrease or cancel subsequent administrations?
- Do they have the expertise to interpret the results of an ECG or liver test? If not, do they have someone on hand who does?
- Are they emphasizing the dangers of overdose for those who use opioids directly before or during treatment?
- Do they have IVs and heart monitors? If so, do they know how to operate them?
- Will a CPR-qualified person be present?
- Are they voicing obscure yet crucial information regarding ibogaines tolerance reset and highlighting why it's vital that relapsed patients return only to novice doses of opioids to avoid overdose?
- Can they advise on the different time periods required to transition from long to short-acting opiates? Do they understand the variables inherent in methadone and buprenorphine consumption?
- Are they asking a patient's age?
- Are they asking the extent to which one's body has been damaged by alcohol?
- Are they asking whether a patient combines crystal meth with heroin or cocaine?
- Is there any inquiry into a patient's psychiatric history? Are they being asked whether they are taking antidepressants or benzodiazepines?

These are just a sample of the questions that need to be resolved prior to ibogaine-assisted detoxification from drugs. The truth is that many providers, particularly in the earlier days, provided treatment in either ignorance or willful neglect of the dangers and still walked away with a clean sheet. Likewise, the number of desperate addicts who have shunned protocol and experienced a successful outcome is high. Despite a decrease in both patients and providers who play it fast and loose, it's fair to assume that such practices still occur, often without serious incident. However, it's also safe to assume that the next time a headline appears reporting an ibogaine-related death, one or both of these scenarios are to blame; a lack of provider experience regarding detox's physiological complexities or an addict who misrepresented their condition.

Set and Setting

A typical Bwiti initiation ceremony may feature dancers in masks and body paint, exotic musical instruments, offbeat percussive rhythms, and surreal artifacts and elements that may prompt the average LSD or psilocybin user to run for the door.

Iboga and ibogaine are different. Unlike traditional psychedelics, whereby the subject is able (and often required) to interact with the world around them, ibogaine treatment is a deeply personal journey into one's own headspace. The traditional notion of "set" and "setting" advocates good people in a comfortable environment. Although these remain essential aspects of any ibogaine treatment, the fact that the subject is flat out, unaware of the outside world means "set and setting" do not apply in quite the same manner as in other psychedelic scenarios.

The clinical setting will likely be at night, in a dark room, with an eye mask to ensure one's visual field is limited to the visions. The same applies to noise. Imagine experiencing an incredible dream, only to be awoken by your alarm clock just as the narrative reaches its peak. While deep in the experience, the last thing the subject needs is the background sounds of traffic noise, roadworks, dogs barking, people talking, or anything else that may interrupt the narrative continuity of their experience.

In addition to decreasing pre-treatment anxiety, a soothing, comfortable environment will make for a more relaxed experience both during and after the journey. Although the period is usually less, it is not unheard of for people to remain in bed for up to a few days afterward.

The duty of care incumbent on the provider should always outweigh that of the patient. To experienced providers, the aforementioned concerns are basic procedures and will likely be taken care of well in advance.

Practical Experience

The "provider" label technically includes anyone who "provides" ibogaine. This includes friends, strangers, well-intentioned novices, and those who realize they can turn a quick buck by ordering ibogaine from the web and embarking on a colorful new career.

Many providers are ex-addicts themselves. This double-edged sword can either hurt or heal. Following successful treatment, some people become so enamored with ibogaine they feel it their God-given task to help others. Unless such decisions are taken with humility and a desire to learn, such individuals are often nowhere near qualified for the job. In some cases, their lives are still in disarray, and they may require far more healing before they can even consider helping others.

Conversely, there are qualified ex-addicts turned providers. For these guys, ibogaine's life-changing capabilities extended way beyond getting clean. Often, their treatment emblazoned upon them a desire to study, and then serve with respect, humility, and the wish to continue often in the face of financial and personal hardship. Their familiarity with the pain, frustration, hopelessness, and desperation of addiction goes beyond an academic query. They have lived it for themselves. In some cases, this experience marks them as perfect candidates to hold a newcomer's hand. Crucially, it confers on them the ability to empathize.

Seasoned providers should be on hand to guide clients the moment they commit to the process. They should be available to provide answers on subjects ranging from detox tips, diet, anxiety management, to details a patient may not have considered, such as travel, visa requirements, airport pickups, and local travel to the treatment center.

When a client arrives, they may be depressed or nervous. More importantly, they may be entering withdrawal, and suffering cramps, nausea, vomiting, and more. In addition to knowing if, when, and how to medicate them safely, experienced providers understand the need for rest, hydration, and the importance of having a trustworthy person on hand if they're feeling low.

Having experienced everything from Ritalin to 5-MEO-DMT, some hardcore drug users may think there's no high left under the sun they aren't familiar with. This self-assurance is shattered the moment the ibogaine begins to curveball through their system. To some, its potency, along with the sheer weirdness of what's unfolding, can provoke utter bewilderment and even mortal panic.

Under ibogaine, a person's heart slows. Then, their psychological frequency and perceptual range shift irreversibly in the direction of the supernaturally strange. At this stage, it's not uncommon for patients to question whether ibogaine was a monumentally lousy idea. Some may even believe that the end is nigh. As such, the reassuring presence and calming voice of someone who understands such feelings to be a standard part of the package can be essential.

As the experience progresses, the provider's role essentially becomes that of a babysitter. They are attentive, professional, caring, and familiar with responding to practical matters. Experienced providers aren't going to get queasy about mopping up vomit or mind helping you to the bathroom if needed.

After the patient has eased into the experience, the provider's role is to observe from afar. A good provider understands their charge is deep into realms they may later recollect as "magic" and then concede even that description falls short. They know this is no time to interrupt. Their job is to quietly monitor the person's condition, identify if and when more medicine is required, and watch for subtle signs of their return to waking consciousness.

Eventually, ibogaine's immediate effects will fade, and the subject will begin to stir. Hopefully, their newfound psychological and physiological wellbeing will be a source of pride. Accompanying this may be a sense of baffled disorientation, physical weakness, and zero desire to spring out of bed. An experienced provider knows this to be a time for a patient to be left alone with one's thoughts. Still, they should also make regular progress checks, help with movement if necessary, and provide nourishment if requested.

The confidence, competence, and intuitiveness required to be a good provider comes only with time. However, the same could be said of a doctor, lawyer, engineer, or almost any other profession. When it comes to responsible ibogaine administration, there remains a subtle range of *x-factor* characteristics and personality traits that separates the great from the average. These include compassion, non-judgment, empathy, altruism, selfless devotion, and a simple yet sincere desire to improve the world one small step at a time via promoting mental and physical health in others. These are the qualities of a healer.

From the Greek word *empatheia* (from em- 'in' + pathos 'feeling'), "empathy" means *"the ability to understand and share the feelings of another."* This is a common, often undervalued character trait of individuals in professions and roles that demand a high capacity for caring about others. Examples include nursing, aid work, counseling, and other professions aimed at helping others, regardless of background, race, class, gender, or circumstance, and with no preconceived judgments regarding how bad luck came to befall them.

Often, these healers possess a strong, innate sense of right and wrong, a passionate idealism, underscored by a quiet confidence that despite the world often being a cruel place, there remains a beauty in life accessible to all, especially those at rock bottom who have forgotten how to stand. Often in the face of personal and financial discomfort and sometimes even ridicule from the mainstream medical establishment, these people forge ahead. For some, this sacrifice of comfort and material gains is offset by the personal rewards derived from helping to lift others from physical or mental anguish. They value quality over quantity and apply their ability to recognize pain in supporting others through their healing journey.

A final essential trait to look for in an ibogaine provider is humility. While the world's leading brain surgeon may be entitled to a degree of hubris, similar qualities in an ibogaine provider are an immediate red flag. True healers, and by extension, skilled ibogaine providers, know that the "true healer" is the plant itself. Blowing their own horn is against their nature, instead offering themselves as conduits for an immensely powerful, sacred medicine to be approached and administered with humility and reverence.

9

AFTERCARE

Temporarily breaking clear from the pull of addictive drugs is a significant accomplishment in its own right. But for many, the physical detox is merely the first step on the path to full recovery. The road ahead is littered with hidden booby traps and the literal and figurative corpses of those who never made it to the end.

To make the finish line will require a map, with the nature and location of these traps clearly marked. Thanks to addiction specialists, psychologists, dedicated ibogaine providers, and recovered addicts who have stayed the course, this map is now the most accurate and detailed it has ever been. It should be followed and kept close to hand.

Ultimately, this is a treasure map. Unlike the movies, it doesn't feature exotic locations in rain forests or ancient Egyptian ruins. Quite the opposite. This terrain is infinitely more testing than anything in film or on television. It is the world of the mundane. A place where psychological trauma is rife. A place which, for many, the notion of existential meaning or true purpose is merely a distant and seductive siren song on daily repeat from TV screens and billboards. A place where dopamine stimulating elements from social media through to vice, drink, and drugs lurk around every corner. It is the world of everyday existence, where the search for meaning must be undertaken without the aid of damaging and addictive props to lean on.

Many ibogaine providers offer some manner of immediate aftercare for patients. Additionally, increased numbers returning from Costa Rica, Mexico, and beyond have given rise to a few US-based facilities set up specifically to provide immediate post-treatment aftercare.

While laudable in its own right, many of those returning from foreign shores have often spent what little they had on ibogaine treatment, rendering extended stays at treatment centers beyond their financial means. Such individuals need to remember that help is at hand and that their ibogaine treatment means they are already off to the best possible head start.

There is no single blanket aftercare treatment considered optimal for everyone. What works for one individual may not be suitable for another. The following information contains some of the therapies and activities proven to help recover from substance dependence, alcohol abuse, and more. This is far from the last word on the subject. Nevertheless, it contains a range of suggested practices to aid the quest towards sobriety and freedom from drug addiction.

During recovery, it's best to be armed with as many tools as possible. Identifying the optimal treatment modalities may require a little digging. However, one thing the professionals unanimously agree upon is this: The best period to begin exploring these modalities is immediately following ibogaine treatment, while the post-treatment serotonin glow still burns bright and before the "window of opportunity" closes.

Much has been written about this mythical post-treatment window of opportunity. During this period, it's easy to believe that anything, including freedom from addiction, is possible.

Truly, this is a special period in which to change the habits and patterns associated with addiction, partake in new activities, and establish the operational framework for a drug-free way of life. Like muscle memory, only by conscious repetition of these activities and choices will the psychological liberation from addiction eventually emerge.

Self-Belief

This "window of opportunity," which is basically a finite, noribogaine assisted head-start, will eventually close. Thereafter, it's essential that the post-treatment flame of self-belief is not extinguished and supplanted by self-doubt.

Addiction often goes hand-in-hand with low self-esteem, a diminished sense of self-worth, and a nagging voice in one's head whispering, *who are you to think you deserve the life you desire?*" Ibogaine's ability to shush such negative voices, to change the stories you tell yourself about yourself, is powerful and persuasive. As time goes by, replacing these voices with positive affirmations such as *"I am a good person worthy of happiness, respect, and freedom from addiction"* becomes second nature. Once banished, one will realize themselves more capable than they could ever have imagined, braver than they think, and stronger than the substances that kept them in chains. This newfound courage and strength may well be the springboard from which incredible things are achieved.

Therein lies the beauty of self-belief. The power it confers represents the ultimate positive feedback loop that builds on itself day after day. The more positive decisions and changes one makes, and the more one acts upon the plan they set for themselves, the more able and energized they feel to keep building and keep working towards goals previously considered impossible. Although arriving at such a place can be difficult, the rewards can be extensive.

Social Triggers

Most ex-smokers will tell you the toughest hurdle with quitting cigarettes is the "associative" triggers. These cigarettes are commonly the post-meal, during phone calls, and morning coffee smokes, all of which have become a regimented part of their habit.

The addiction triumvirate consists of the substance, the person, and the context. Just like a cigarette smoker feels the urge to light up after sex or the moment they crack open a beer, those recovering from hard drug use are in for the same urges if they continue to hang out with their old drug friends in the same environments they associate with past drug use.

The best advice may be to steer clear of such situations, even if that costs a person their entire circle of friends. Some individuals even move to a new city. However, for many more, this may be unrealistic. In the highly likely event one encounters such a trigger-rich scenario, the good news may be that your post-ibogaine desire to re-engage with these behaviors may only be psychological and not skin-crawlingly physical. Nevertheless, at this stage of recovery, many forget the mind's power to sell them *one last hit for old times sake.*

Successful recoverees have learned to anticipate, identify, and react accordingly whenever a trigger presents itself. Before arriving at this level of disciplined self-awareness, the best course of action is to consciously and actively avoid the old social circles and the trigger-rich environments.

Therapy

Although the ibogaine experience may unmask the underlying psychological complexities of one's plight, attempts to push ahead without adequately addressing these issues can end in relapse. If left to fester, the same pains and anxieties will eventually return. Pain relief will be sought after. This is why counseling and/or therapy is considered a key factor in addiction recovery. As cartographers of the human psyche, who better to help draw the required road map than a qualified and experienced psychotherapist?

Cognitive-Behavioral Therapy

Cognitive-behavioral therapists are skilled in training people to anticipate and identify emotions, thoughts, moods, and cues that stimulate cravings. If they're good at their job, they will teach clients how to identify, avoid, and, if necessary, react to that which would prompt a return to substance abuse. They will work with the patient to replace the associated emotions with positive, alternative thought patterns that underlie healthier real-world choices and outcomes.

Besides being a valuable recovery aid, the recovering addict may well find CBT's value extends way beyond addiction recovery. CBT therapy results may last a lifetime. If applied correctly, they may go on to deliver a patient to a place where the world is truly their oyster.

Individual Therapy & Counseling

Optimally, recovering addicts should have this in place long before ibogaine treatment and should begin to visit, or revisit their therapist at the first available post-treatment opportunity.

In addition to their ability to help process trauma, a skilled therapist can help teach a person to explore the source of their anxiety and thus change the real-world consequences of thoughts, attitudes, and beliefs.

Group Therapy

Group therapy is effective at combating the feelings of loneliness that often catalyze a return to using drugs. A group can promote a "we're all in this together mentality" and reassure those feeling isolated that they are not alone. The therapeutic community has long known that the mere act of articulating feelings and frustrations can serve as an invaluable cathartic release. The venting of these emotions while surrounded by a circle of non-judgmental peers, bonded by a common goal, can create a powerful and effective setting for building healthy mutual relationships, drawing inspiration and strength, and giving and receiving practical wisdom.

In addition to the wealth of experience-based advice on offer from other group members, attendees may well find themselves able to also offer invaluable guidance to those around them. It may even be the perfect scenario in which to share details of one's ibogaine experience. For those who are thinking of ibogaine treatment but yet to experience it, the presence of someone who has taken ibogaine and is happy to share their thoughts, feelings, and guidance on the subject may be reassuring. Often, the act of sharing one's experience to assist others can serve as a mighty boost to the self-esteem of those imparting their knowledge. Maybe this is why many of those who freed themselves from addictions go on to work in the associated areas of counseling and therapy.

Couples and Family Therapy

Rarely is it only the addicted individual whose life is turned upside down by their condition. All too often, family members are also heavily impacted, with particularly detrimental effects where opioids or alcohol are involved.

The therapeutic setting offers a safe space for the patient and their family members to learn about addiction recovery dynamics. It provides the opportunity to heal and move on from past problems, improve the home environment, and implement the necessary positive changes to give the patient the best chance of achieving their goal.

The same logic applies to couples' therapy. One person's addiction can leave one or both partners confused, angry, and unable to communicate the nature of their frustrations effectively.

Couples' and/or family therapy provides a range of valuable benefits, including a general environment of support. It can also help to heal any wounds that a loved ones´ addiction has inflicted on those closest to them.

Social Support

Although self-belief must ultimately come from within, it's impossible to overstate the value of social support, particularly during periods of fear and perceived isolation. Countless studies have shown that support from friends, family, and peers plays a crucial role in helping recovering addicts stay the course.

Family members are often all too familiar with the consequences, pitfalls, and hallmarks of addiction. They involuntarily become experts at spotting relapse signals in advance and recognizing situations that could trigger a return to alcohol or drugs. Family, friends, and positive people who bring out one's best, and support ideas, dreams, and ambitions beyond the confines of addiction and recovery are essential. By helping to keep the post-ibogaine flame of hope burning, it is these people who can provide the encouragement necessary to remind an addict that change is possible.

During recovery, ex-addicts should surround themselves with people they know, love, trust, and vice-versa. This doesn't include old drug pals, no matter how strong the connection. If addiction's consequences included the loss of certain sober friends, then maybe take a leaf from the Alcoholics Anonymous game-plan and try to reconnect. There are many good reasons to make amends with people during this period. Having a clean, sober person in one's corner is just one of them.

Ibogaine Booster Doses

In most cases, the lingering presence of noribogaine is enough to stave off short-term cravings. In some cases, selective administration of ibogaine booster doses, which are essentially small, non-psychoactive measurements, can be highly beneficial in suppressing lingering cravings.

By effectively prolonging the treatment and helping to maintain mood, clarity, and perspective, these boosters can also help with any unresolved emotional issues that may emerge as the patient transitions back into everyday life.

Boosters pose practical and safety concerns. If a patient receives these doses at the treatment center, one would expect the provider to understand safe dosing requirements. If a patient requires further booster doses following their departure from the clinic, some providers may equip them with both the medicine and the necessary dosing information. It is important to remember that if combining ibogaine with certain other substances, the best-case scenario may be that ibogaine is rendered ineffective. The worst-case scenario? Death.

As with the flood dose, mental preparation and intent setting will boost the efficacy of these treatments.

Art

The list of famous artists, even geniuses who were addicted to alcohol or drugs, is endless. Whether the production of great art and the existential dissatisfaction that underlies addiction go hand-in-hand is a long conversation. Regardless, art is not a luxury reserved for the creative elite. You don't have to be Amy Winehouse, Jon Bonham, or Vincent Van Gogh to understand that the act of producing music, or painting, writing, drawing, dancing, and acting can permeate muted parts of the soul that crave to communicate in mediums beyond language.

Whether practiced alone or in a group, formal art therapy or fun experimentation can be a powerful creative outlet for those recovering from addiction. It provides a non-conversational, deeply personal means of gently coaxing ingrained trauma into the spotlight. Trauma is often stored in the same mysterious places that art, like therapy or psychedelics, has a unique ability to tap into. Once pierced, the contents that spill from the resulting hole can serve as a powerful means of self-expression and a valuable tool to explore, understand and resolve problems that the intellect is powerless to grasp. One may even discover their inner artist to be more proficient than they ever imagined and create things that resonate so personally and powerfully that the love for the creative process will take residence in the domain formerly inhabited by drugs and alcohol.

Interestingly, many users of psychedelics report receiving

firm directives to incorporate artistic pursuit as a standard day-to-day practice in their lives. For a few, so clear is this message they have been known to immediately trade a steady job for a leap-of-faith in pursuit of their bliss.

Exercise

Dopamine and serotonin are the organic "feel-good" chemicals that play a major role in reward-motivated behavior. Persistent substance abuse hard-wires the relevant neuro-pathways to associate the gratification once supplied by these natural compounds with drugs. Additionally, drug addiction depletes the brain's natural dopamine supply, sparking feelings of sadness and low self-esteem. In terms of contributing relapse factors, this dopamine and serotonin deficit is a chief offender.

The recovery process involves rerouting and reopening the original neuropathways and replenishing the biochemicals that should be, and eventually will be, traversing these channels.

Hopefully, ibogaine will restore these channels and neurotransmitters to a pre-addicted state. However, the area of the brain that houses entrenched behavioral patterns is far removed from the dopamine and serotonin systems. Over time, this disconnect may emerge as an inner voice eulogizing a drug-fueled joyride down memory lane, particularly if dopamine production isn't firing on all cylinders. During this period, it's essential to engage in activities that promote natural dopamine and serotonin production.

The quickest and most effective way of guaranteeing the rapid release of dopamine and serotonin is through exercise. It does the same thing as drugs, minus the catastrophic side effects. Aerobic exercise, in particular, is known to increase serotonin.

For some, particularly opioid-based painkiller addicts,

certain forms of intense exercise may be off the table. Luckily, many forms of low-impact exercise such as yoga or tai-chi can be effective.

If even these pursuits are too rigorous, it's essential to keep busy. Any recovering addict will attest to the power of boredom as a major relapse trigger. Whether it be voluntary work, taking walks, or embarking on a new area of study, finding an enjoyable activity that deflects one's mind and attention from the desire to return to old patterns is essential.

Spirituality

Alcoholics Anonymous has occasionally come under fire from groups who perceive their methods as dogmatic and exclusive or because of accusations that their only acceptable spiritual path is through Jesus. Regardless of arguments for or against (and there exists both), to allow AA's central message to become distorted by semantics would be the proverbial equivalent of throwing the baby Jesus out with the bathwater.

When AA began in the mid-1930s, Bill Wilson, AA's co-founder, initially struggled with the concept that one substance could be used to overcome addiction to another. His position changed following his first acid trip at the Veterans Administration hospital in Los Angeles on 29 August 1956. Thereafter, he was convinced that psychedelics could help addicts to experience a helpful spiritual awakening on the path to recovery.

Decades on, some still argue the type of "spirituality" iboga or other psychedelics may bequeath is not considered ideally suited to addiction recovery. Some would agree, while others would call such an assertion utter garbage. In their defense, AA may respond that Christianity promotes selflessness, atonement, and other key addiction recovery components that psychedelics do not always catalyze.

Although their theistic leanings have been the target of some valid criticisms, it is not without reason that 6 of the 12 AA steps program refer directly or indirectly to spirituality's power in overcoming addiction. Such beliefs have been echoed by philosophers, therapists, and more for decades, even centuries. This insight was poetically surmised by Carl Jung when discussing how to exorcise the demons of addiction. In his letter to Bill Wilson, he writes:

> "You see, alcohol in Latin is 'spiritus' and you use the same word for the highest religious experience as well as for the most depraving poison. The helpful formula, therefore, is: spiritus contra spiritum."[73, 74]

Jung means that *spiritus*, or the "low spirits" that possess those who drink the "spirits," can be countered *(contra)* only by religious experience, or *spiritum*, meaning the "higher spirits." Jung was referring to alcohol, but he could just as well have been talking about opium, cocaine, or other substances. Interestingly, Jung's words bear striking similarities with the shamanistic and animistic perspectives pertaining to the spirit of all plants, both benevolent and malevolent.

Jung believed these cravings stemmed from *"the spiritual thirst of our being for wholeness, expressed in medieval language, the union with God."*[75] He was not alone in his beliefs. Philosophers, theologists, addiction specialists, even neuroscientists have argued that this yearning for oneness with "the whole," this desire to fill the gap created in the wake of man's separation from God, or "spirit," is precisely what underlies the motivation to turn to harmful substances and activities. In his book,

The Neuroscience of Religious Experience, neuroscientist Patrick McNamara even goes so far as to argue that humankind's desire to unify these fractured elements may be the foundation for all religious beliefs. If true, it follows that reunification with one's spiritual side is a huge step in leaving these temporarily pleasurable yet highly addictive elements behind.[76]

Psychiatrist and prominent psychedelic researcher, Stanislav Grof, wrote that despite administering high doses of LSD to subjects that included materialist scientists and atheists, he had yet to encounter a single individual *"whose skepticism and cynicism about spirituality would survive such an experience."*[77] Now, take that concept, and apply it to iboga, a compound so powerful and spiritually significant as to become the keystone of an entire Central African practice. Little wonder then that so many exit the iboga(ine) experience convinced that everything they thought they knew about humankind's spiritual dimensions is either wrong or has been wildly underestimated.

It matters not whether one's spiritual touchstone is Jesus, Buddha, Jediism, nature, or founded in a psychedelic experience which imbues one with a rock-solid conviction that this "higher power" exists. The net result of iboga-induced transcendentalism, as evidenced by the number of people in whom it catalyzed the cessation of everything from cigarettes, to alcohol, to heroin, is similar.

Undoubtedly, it seems that a sense of individual spirituality does indeed provide a highly effective means of fortifying one's sense of purpose while navigating the road to recovery. If some argue that to be a "crutch," then so what? Try telling a guy with a broken leg that he doesn't need one and that hobbling down the road in pain is the only noble means of addressing his plight.

Although iboga is known to blow some subjects wide open in terms of spiritual openness and receptivity, it doesn't seem to exert influence on which spiritual path, if any, to take. The experience seems to leave the user to conclude which works best for them. Through this lens, does it not seem a comic irony that following their iboga(ine) journey, some people, including some Bwiti sects, have been inspired to sign on to the very religion that has demonized and tried to eradicate iboga and its practitioners? Consequently, one can't help wonder how AA or missionaries in the Congo would react to receiving Christ via a "pagan root." Or (given that the same logic implies his dad planted it there), what kind of response Christ himself would have?

These musings aside, the point remains that anyone looking to truly beat addiction might think seriously about opening their heart and mind to some manner of spiritual practice. For an unlikely few, this may be journeying to India to meditate in a cave for a decade. For others, it may be a walk through the forest to revel in nature. In addition to both the health benefits and the value as a recovery tool, one may just tap into elements of their being erroneously dismissed as the stuff of religious dogma or science fiction. What does one have to lose? Nothing. What does one have to gain? Well, that's something they must find out for themselves.

For many people, this 'higher power' concept may have zero to do with God or any other deity. It is often simply a question of rising above their own ego and heeding a call to serve something other than themselves and their own immediate desires.

III

REMEMBERING
DISMEMBERMENT

10

WHY THE PAIN?

"What was it that did in reality make me an opium eater? Misery, blank desolation, abiding darkness."[78]

Thomas De Quincey

The opening chapter of this book highlighted the hurdles in defining iboga – a compound that exists at the outer limits of academic knowledge and eludes most attempts to account for its actions. It's no small irony then that iboga could be such a promising weapon in the fight against a condition whose complex components have long rendered it beyond the confines of scientific or medical diagnosis.

The go-to definition of addiction as a *"neurological disorder characterized by compulsive engagement in rewarding stimuli despite negative outcomes,"* is an attempt to reduce a mystery where the whole is far greater than the sum of the parts.

That said, in recent decades, theories have emerged identifying one of addiction's most crucial components. While they may sound new, they echo wisdom outlined in texts dating back hundreds, if not thousands of years. In lockstep with iboga research, some of the best findings are coming not from the laboratories but from those tasked with exploring humankind's psyches and souls.

Nowadays, the list of superb written works surrounding the nature and treatment of addiction is growing. This book is not one of them and makes no pretense at being such. Thankfully, the chief culprit these theories identify (although still complex in its own right) is more easily singled out.

At the turn of the 20th century, the Downtown Eastside (DTES) of Vancouver, Canada, was the city's political and cultural nerve center. As industry shifted west, the DTES witnessed a steady decrease in affluence. In the 1980s, this decline became a plummeting downward spiral. Funding for mental health patients and social housing took a nose-dive while sex work, crime, and homelessness skyrocketed. Whether subsequent soaring cases of hard-drug abuse represented the chicken or the egg would take decades of controversial debate to ascertain. At the time, one thing not up for debate was the social consequences of this downturn.

Currently, the DTES is home to one of the most densely confined communities of hard-drug users in the world. If any silver lining to the cloud floating over the DTES exists, it's that the area would consequently become a fertile breeding ground for some of the world's most well-informed addiction psychologists and researchers. In addition to creating innovative harm-reduction programs, these individuals spearheaded the shift in perspectives on drug addiction and helped shatter the dogma on which the failed "war on drugs" was founded. Arguably, one of the most influential researchers to come from this area was Bruce K. Alexander, a Vancouver psychologist.

In 1981, Alexander conducted an experiment that would revolutionize our understanding of drug addiction. Before this, most data had come from animal studies. Specifically, studies designed to measure a rat's desire to consume hard drugs when given the opportunity.

It was thought the optimal way to measure this was by tethering a rat to the ceiling of a small box, insert button-activated needles containing heroin, morphine, cocaine, and amphetamine into their veins, and let them have at it. Have at it they did and addicted they became. Researchers concluded that drug addiction was due solely to the addictive chemical lure of these substances. Their chemical properties alone were enough to transform every user, regardless of environment, background, race, or even species, into a hopelessly enslaved addict. During the 1970s, these conclusions fit neatly with the cultural climates prevailing narrative and were presented as Exhibit A by advocates of the war on drugs. These substances were evil and must be wiped from the face of the earth. Drug addicts weren't much different. Case closed.

Enter Bruce K. Alexander. Alexander's controversial hypothesis was that substance abuse was less about the addictive properties of the drugs and more to do with the living conditions and resultant emotional and mental health of those taking them. His "Rat Park" experiment was based on the simple premise that rats, like humans, are social creatures. Like humans, rats get depressed and go insane when placed in solitary confinement and denied basic biological needs. In other words, precisely the kind of environment in which they'd previously been confined.

Traditionally, the lab rats' accommodation was the "Skinner box." Until Rat Park came along, these hellishly tiny, stimulation-free dungeons were the only home they had ever known. Compared with the Skinner boxes, Rat Park was a paradise, a veritable Disneyland of space, food, water, toys, interaction, and lots of room to mate.

The short version of this story goes like this. To begin, Alexander divided the rats into groups. The luckier Rat Park residents were able to choose between two water dispensers. One contained plain tap water. The other contained water infused with a morphine solution. The other group drew the short straw. They were condemned to the Skinner boxes and offered the same beverage menu. Guess which group immediately began sucking back the mind-numbing morphine?

Unlike their pound-bound counterparts, the rats with unbridled access to Rat Park's amenities chose the tap water. Sometime later, the drug-addicted jailhouse rats gained reprieve and were sent to live in Rat Park. Despite that morphine remained available, they instead shunned the drugs in favor of plain water, even opting to suffer voluntary opiate withdrawal.

Over time, the Rat Park study has drawn both criticism and support. Although methodological flaws were noted, these criticisms were increasingly drowned out by further findings that supported those from Rat Park.[79]

But, argued critics, what about the fact that rats and humans are light years apart in terms of emotional and cognitive development?

FIGHTING A WAR....ON DRUGS!

Five years after Bruce Alexander published his findings, a Harvard psychoanalyst named Norman Zinberg published his book *Drug, Set, and Setting: The Basis for Controlled Intoxicant Use.* This work was based on more than two decades of research into how different people interacted with different psychoactive drugs. Zinberg's investigations focused on US soldiers in Vietnam, many of whom had engaged in heavy opium use to escape the hellish daily reality of war. According to the old perspective, it was assumed these men would continue using heroin upon their return home. In contrast, Zinberg found 88% ceased their habit immediately.[80] Zinberg concluded that although we all have the neural make-up required to become addicts, very few do.

The work of Alexander, Zinberg, and others showed that creatures condemned to a life of misery would embrace any alternative dopamine source with gusto. Conversely, those not subject to feelings of powerlessness, hopelessness, and loneliness are far better equipped to resist the pull of addictive drugs. Their findings laid waste to the narrative that had stood for decades. So why did drug addiction skyrocket in subsequent decades?

In late 2017, US health secretary Tom Price tweeted, *"We're losing more people to drug overdoses each year than we lost during the entire Vietnam War."*[81] Two years earlier, the DEA reported overdoses from heroin and prescription drugs had "reached epidemic levels."[82] In the same year, it was reported that annual overdose-related fatalities in the US had surpassed the number of deaths from both firearms and car accidents.[83] Two-thirds of these fatalities stemmed from opioid abuse.[84]

After Alexander and Zinberg released their groundbreaking findings, it would be reasonable to conclude this would help stem the rising tide of opioid addiction. So, why has the number of substance-addicted individuals, particularly opioid addicts, risen higher than at any point in human history? According to renowned addiction expert Gabor Mate, if opioids are essentially nothing more than painkillers, then the real question is not why the addiction, but why the pain?[85]

In 1994, Deborah Mash became the first and only scientist to receive FDA approval to begin ibogaine research in the United States. Eventually, funding cuts and pressure to axe all ibogaine-related research prompted Mash to scout a new location from which to continue her work. She settled in the Caribbean. Here, she was able to treat more than 300 patients and collate essential data on ibogaines efficacy. Her work brought to light the crucial and previously overlooked role of aftercare for those returning from ibogaine treatment.

In an interview with the Psychedelic Times, Mash was adamant that her findings reaffirmed what the Rat Park experiment had shown decades earlier; that addiction mainly affects those trying to plug a hole in their soul caused by trauma.[86]

Based on her encounters, Mash concluded that substance abuse represents a self-medicating solution to combat *"anxiety, depression, bipolar disorder, borderline personality disorder, and OCD."*[87] In addition to latent mental disorders, said Mash, many of those she treated suffered from *"traumas, PTSD, childhood abuse, sexual abuse, and childhood neglect."*[88] Essentially, drugs and alcohol represented a dilapidated getaway vehicle needed to outrun a much deeper problem whose ability to keep chase was tireless. Like all vehicles, it needed consistent refueling.

Some years later, the subject of early trauma and the role it plays in shaping the lives of addicts would finally begin to gain the recognition, if not yet the required level of action, it deserved.

HUNGRY GHOSTS

Once again, it was the drug-ravaged streets of Vancouver's east side, long since a fertile incubator of addiction expertise, that would spur Canadian physician and early childhood trauma specialist Gabor Mate to produce some of the most poignant and influential findings ever.

The title of Mates deeply compassionate 2008 book: *In the Realm of Hungry Ghosts: Close Encounters with Addiction*, refers to the Buddhist wheel of life. In Buddhist literature, each of the wheel's six domains represents a different facet of the human condition. One of these realms is the dwelling of creatures who perpetually crave to satiate their appetite for meaning via the pursuit of the meaningless. Said to be souls whose existential quagmire resulted from neglect or abandonment, this is the realm of the hungry ghosts. It is, affirms Mate, the realm of addiction – a metaphorical comparison arrived at based on two decades of working alongside severely addicted, emotionally destitute inhabitants of East Vancouver's skid row.

Gabor Mate was not the first to observe the link between severe addiction and childhood trauma. However, his work on the influence that childhood trauma plays in one's decision-making process arguably shifted the conversation from the specialists to the mainstream. He argues that the psychological components that lead to addiction take root in the formative years.

Mate delivers a compassionate, judgment-free explanation that trauma often traces back to the parents. Knowingly or otherwise, by projecting their own stresses onto their children, or failing to sufficiently convey love, they created a vacuum in their children to be plugged and pacified by elements promising to bridge the resultant emotional gap.

Importantly, Mate acknowledges that parental influences are not always the prime culprit and notes cases of addicts raised in healthy environments yet suffered abuse – sexual, physical, emotional, or otherwise – from outsiders. He also acknowledges that the subject is far from clear-cut and that addiction is often driven by a complex interaction of multiple contributing factors.

Mate clarifies that he is not trying to ascribe blame but to highlight that those suffering from addiction are often in genuine, unrelenting emotional pain. As these seeds grow, the emotional scars harden and eventually manifest themselves in dysfunction, isolation, loneliness, and despairing confusion at one's inability to identify or articulate where the issues begin and end. Among this group are those who will turn to anything, even the ingestion of chemical waste, in a bid to blank out the sorrow of their existence.

SPIRITUAL POVERTY

Three decades after Rat Park showed that social conditions and the resultant emotional and mental health were crucial precursors to addiction, a book was published that took a new perspective on an age-old problem. The author was none other than Rat Park architect himself: Bruce K. Alexander.

In his 2008 book *The Globalization of Addiction: A Study in Poverty of the Spirit,* Alexander argues that although the range of globalized addictions includes drugs and alcohol, it is a mistake to view the source, role, or destructive potential of these as any different to *"gambling, love, power-seeking, religious or political zeal, work, food, video game playing, internet surfing, pornography, retail therapy,"* and more.[89]

Alexander sums up these behavioral tendencies as:

> "overwhelming and harmful involvement with any pursuit whatsoever that is harmful to the addicted person, to society, or to both."[90]

These addictions, argues Alexander, can consume every aspect of a person's life, including:

> "The conscious, unconscious, intellectual, emotional, behavioral, social and spiritual – just as severe drug and alcohol addiction can."[91]

Alexander agrees with Gabor Mate, that isolated incidents of trauma can lead to addiction. However, he argues a stressful home life, fractured communities, and the ongoing hardships that run rife throughout dispossessed areas are more powerful driving forces of addiction.

According to Alexander, the ringleader of this cultural and community deterioration is the global spread of free markets. For centuries, key community, spiritual, political, and social institutions prioritized individual and community well-being over material gains. As free markets spread, these institutions sold their souls to an unstoppable, unforgiving, free-market capitalist ideology predicated on stress, competition, and social Darwinism.

The hierarchical nature of this system offers untold benefits for those able to adapt and thrive under it. However, these individuals are far outnumbered by those unable or unwilling to tow the materialist line. As a result, many are often left out in the cold. This frozen social, economic, and cultural wasteland is, according to Alexander, the perfect environment for the growth of addiction's precursor; "social dislocation."

SOCIAL DISLOCATION

Dislocation, says Alexander, has been given many names, perhaps the most common being "alienation" or "disconnection."[92] In this context, 'dislocation' refers to:

> "the experience of a void that can be described on at least three levels. In social terms, it is the absence of enduring and sustaining connections between individuals and their families and/or

local societies, nations, occupations, traditions, physical environments, and Gods. In existential terms, it is the absence of feelings of belonging, identity, meaning, or purpose. In spiritual terms, it is the experience of poverty of the spirit, home-lessness of the soul, or being forgotten by God."[93]

The complex, multi-faceted nature of this sweeping social malaise and decayed sense of belonging often renders the real-world consequences of dislocation all but impossible for the average Joe to even identify, let alone articulate or resist.

"Strong people can endure dislocation for a time," says Alexander. "However, severe, prolonged dislo-cation eventually leads to unbearable despair, shame, emotional anguish, boredom, and bewilderment."[94]

MEANING MACHINES

Once upon a time, Homo Sapiens began to self-reflect. Our arrival at self-awareness marked the beginning of a neverending search to find answers to big questions, like God, the stars, the animals, the universe, and our place in it. In the absence of real knowledge, we told stories. From orally passed hunter-gatherer tales to the first Sumerian writings, from Shakespeare to Spiel-berg, these stories became the literal, symbolic, cultural, and institutional backbone of civilization. The human search for meaning was and still is, guided by the stories we told ourselves about ourselves. Until comparatively recently, these narratives largely ascribed value to all humans, and supported and cele-brated social, cultural, and spiritual wholeness.

Removing these vital components, argues Alexander, leaves many people struggling to find meaning. They feel confused, dispossessed, and as if they exist in the metaphorical equivalent of the Skinner Box. When social, cultural, and spiritual wholeness fades away, and any sense of meaning evaporates, low-hanging existential fruits such as drugs, alcohol, relationships, shopping, and social media become ripe for the picking.

Essentially, addiction stems from a state of spiritual destitution so extreme that the person is willing to embrace anything able to temporarily anesthetize their existential angst. Although Gabor Mate argues the components of addiction are wide-ranging, his overall conclusion is that at its most fundamental level, addiction is a spiritual experience, or rather, the absence of one.

TRIBES VS COLONIES

Gabor Mate notes that the most obvious example of addictive patterns emerging after the destruction of traditional relationships, family clans, and time-honored value systems that secured people's sense of belonging, is among indigenous peoples subject to colonization by western powers.[95]

Countless examples of such societies exist. However, being from Vancouver, Mate draws from communities he is familiar with working alongside. Namely, the once vibrant native Canadian communities where members had roles, expectations, and identities since time immemorial.

Prior to European contact, the native hunter-gatherer cultures of Canada enjoyed levels of psycho-social integration long since erased from the collective European memory. Their communities were based on shared resources, rituals, rites of passage, religious beliefs, and responsibilities assigned according to merit and individual talents.

Although New World natives happily traded with Europeans, they were sickened by their life-ways and clung to their own cultures with courageous resolution.[96] Avoiding the temptation to romanticize Canadian indigenous peoples as "noble savages," Alexander reminds us that they, too, engaged in war, slavery, and torture. However, every community member had a role to play, and addiction was unheard of.[97]

These lifeways came to a grinding halt the moment militarized western powers set foot on their shores. The colonizers seized their land, placed them on reserves akin to refugee camps, tore apart their families, and outlawed their language, stories, traditional medical practices, and religious ceremonies. Shortly thereafter, alcohol addiction was rife. The parallels with the rat park experiment are glaringly obvious. Bruce Alexander writes:

> "In both cases, the colonizers or the experimenters who provide the drug explain the drug consumption in the isolated environment by saying that the drug is irresistible to the people or the rats. But in both cases, the drug only becomes irresistible when the opportunity for normal social existence is destroyed."[98]

For the Natives of the American continent, this psychological, spiritual, and cultural disfigurement began over 500 years ago, not on Canada's shores but much further South. More specifically, it began on the 12th of October 1492, when an Italian explorer became the first modern European to make landfall on the shores of "New Spain."

11

THE WAR ON DRUGS BEGINS

"From the time of Christopher Columbus onward,
large scale colonization by western powers has
crushed defenseless societies around the globe by
conquest, disease, enslavement, economic exploita-
tion, and religious domination."[99]

Bruce Alexander

Although Christopher Columbus wasn't the first European to 'discover' the Americas, his arrival marked the
beginning of sustained contact between the two continents. It also heralded the birth of the transatlantic slave trade,
the largest campaign of genocide in history, and the acquisition
of wealth beyond imagination for European rulers. In 1496,
Columbus, whose claimed mission statement was the expansion
of Christian creed, wrote in a letter to Queen Isabella of Spain:

"In the name of the holy trinity we can send from
here all the slaves and Brazil-wood which could
be sold."[100]

By the end of the fifteenth century in Europe, the use of psychoactive plants, herbs, and fungi responsible for giving com-
moners a sense of meaning and spirituality, as well as ideas

that challenged centralized power structures, was confined to scattered bands of seditious psychedelic renegades practicing in utmost secrecy, risking their lives in pursuit of the spiritual awakening the Vatican had deemed a capital crime. Just when the Vatican elites began to get comfortable, they encountered a culture that would force them to expand their psychedelic crackdown to unimaginable levels. The war on drugs was about to go global.

The new world's material wealth was rivaled by the richest abundance of psychoactive plants on the planet. Psilocybin-containing mushrooms grew alongside dimethyltryptamine vines (ayahuasca), mescaline-containing cacti (namely San Pedro and peyote), and much more. To the missionary's dismay, it was soon discovered that native belief systems were tightly bound to the spiritual experiences these plants provided. So much reverence and lasting spiritual significance did these potent experiences bestow, any attempt to convince the indigenous peoples to trade their native plant teachers for the Judeo-Christian God, thus trading direct communion for unquestioning faith, was doomed from the outset.

A HOTLINE TO HELL

Spanish and Portuguese settlers faced a huge dilemma. So widespread was the distribution of psychedelic flora that any attempt to eradicate them would be fruitless. Fortunately, the colonists had a powerful weapon to fall back on. The natives' beliefs in spiritual realms and entities not mentioned in scripture automatically placed them in league with Satan. Not only were these "primitives" inclined towards satanic worship, but they also possessed an expansive arsenal of diabolical, naturally-occurring tools with which to contact the prince of darkness directly.

In the 16th century, the earliest reports from missionaries described ayahuasca as the *"work of the devil."*[101] Huachuma (San Pedro) was reported as *"a plant with whose aid the devil is able to strengthen the Indians in their idolatry."*[102]

In 1591, a conquistador physician named Juan de Cárdenas penned the following passage regarding Peyote consumption.

> "In sooth they tell us that peyote, when taken by mouth, will cause the wretch who takes them to lose his wits so severely that he sees the devil among other terrible and fearsome apparitions; and he will be warned (so they say) of things to come, and all this must be tricks and lies of Satanas, whose nature is to deceive, with divine permission, the wretch who on such occasions seeks him."[103]

Seventeenth-Century conquistador writer, Hernando Ruiz de Alarcon, chronicled his observations regarding native consumption of morning glory seeds thus:

> "Ololiuqui is a kind of seed-like lentils produced by a type of vine in this land, which when drunk deprive of the senses, because it is very powerful, and by this means they communicate with the devil, because he talks to them when they are deprived of judgment with the said drink, and deceive them with different hallucinations, and they attribute it to a God they say is inside the seed."[104]

In an attempt to eradicate spiritual traditions practiced since time immemorial, these plant medicines were deemed in direct opposition to scripture and quite literally demonized. Those caught in possession were labeled heretics and doomed to suffer horrific fates at the hands of their captors. One missionary reported:

> "A great many Indians were flogged and sometimes killed when they persisted in using huachuma. One man's eyeballs were said to be gouged out after three days of torture, then the Spaniards cut a crucifix in his belly and turned ravenous dogs loose on his innards."[105]

The Roman Catholic church knew these psychoactive plants to be powerful catalysts of religious dissent. Moreover, as the self-appointed owners of every square inch of land on the planet, the message these plants conveyed, that mankind belonged to the earth, and not the earth to mankind, didn't sit too well with Vatican elites. The solution; to deal with the indigenous native Americans just as they had the early pagans of the west.

12

BWITI AND IBOGA: REMEMBERING DISMEMBERMENT

"In church, they speak of God. With iboga, you live God."[106]

Nengue Me Ndjoung Isidore

In the mid-eighteenth-century, European companies on the lookout for the jackpot combination of "primitive" tribes and valuable resources turned their attention to the resource-rich jungles of Central Africa. In pole-position was the French. Their African-tenancy rights and decreed ownership of every human, animal, or material asset had been signed and sealed by *Eximise Devotionis*, a Papal Bull issued by Pope Alexander VI to assuage French anger after South America went to the Spanish.

Despite a sizeable French presence, two American missionaries, Reverends Wilson and Griswold, became the first Westerners to make contact with the Fang people in June 1842. Wilson considered them:

"vastly superior in their personal appearance to the maritime tribes" and had "no hesitation in pronouncing them the finest Africans I have ever met with."[107, 108]

To the European economic power elites, now massively enriched following centuries of scripture-sanctioned land and resource theft, the egalitarian, non-materialist ways of these traditional cultures denoted them as little more than rabble-rousing socialists.[109] Their worth was measured by their capacity to locate, uproot, stack, and ship natural resources to Europe. They were told the recompense awaiting them in the afterlife far outweighed earthly trivialities such as payment, breaks, or a decent meal.

Much like the Spanish conquistadors, western missionaries and companies in Gabon were faced with a fiercely proud culture whose relationship with the planet remained rooted in symbiosis, respect, and the idea that decimating one's own backyard wasn't necessarily a good thing. Their mythologies were their own, and their ceremonies, community rituals, and rites of passage were solid. They did not succumb to vice, addictions, or disease, had never heard of the agricultural or industrial revolutions, and their collective cultural psyche was unsullied by the Judeo-Christian narratives that dominated Europe thousands of years.

Griffin Du Bellay was a French naval surgeon whose encounters with iboga in the 1860s were the first to be written into the record. In reference to the perceived temperament of West African natives, Bellay wrote;

> "one cannot ignore that they will be very captious subjects and difficult to manage." Bellay noted that although "hospitable enough, they also have a stormy and versatile character served by an industry and energy that few blacks possess."[110]

That these untamed jungle dwellers would present a management challenge was clear from the outset. The mindset of European polite society had evolved somewhat since the days of Christopher Columbus. Suppression of civil disobedience via a swift and corrective bloodbath was no longer considered an appropriate response. Additionally, slave ownership in Europe had by now fallen from grace and been outlawed. For the most part, the Central African tribes were not subjected to the same extreme brutality suffered by their New World counterparts. Nevertheless, the European company directors thought nothing of rounding them up at gunpoint and sending them out to retrieve lumber, rubber, ivory, and more, effectively trading international slavery for domestic.

In attempts to evade the encroaching European powers, and the associated diseases, famine, enslavement, destruction of their villages, and eradication of traditional spiritual practices, some of these people chose to retreat further into the jungles of the Congo Basin. Here, or so the story goes, they formed bonds with the deep forest-dwelling pygmies who revealed to them the mysteries of the iboga plant.[111]

Eventually, the word got out. Expedited by the strong links formed by different tribes slaving away in the lumber camps, rumors of iboga's capabilities spread quickly. After nightfall, workers would meet to partake in iboga ceremonies.[112] When the Fang people eventually returned to their homes, they brought with them knowledge of a mysterious root, consumption of which provided communication with one's dead ancestors. The Bwiti tradition was born.

Bwiti religious ceremonies revolved (and still do) around a plant that facilitates direct access to realms believed to be the domain of dead ancestors and divine entities. Upon return, pilgrims often claim to have experienced an increased sense of existential purpose and self-sovereignty. Clearly, not the kind of personal or group ideology any self-respecting slave owner would wish to encourage. Neither was it an easy dilemma for the missionaries to overcome, particularly when the alternative amounted to a white collared middle-man, peddling an aloof Godhead who wasn't too keen on being seen by his flock.

In response, the missionaries dug out and dusted off the original Roman Catholic playbook. Iboga and other such means of divine communion were deemed pagan idolatry, directly opposed to catholic doctrine at best, outright satanic at worst. Practitioners who shunned Christianity in favor of these Godless primitive rituals were written off as hell-bound heretics.

In 1930, in *Notes Sur le Gabon,* future governor Paul Vuillaume wrote:

> "the practices of Bouiti are harmful to those tribes who adopt it and this is because of the terror that this society exercise over people by committing murders or by violating tombs in order to obtain human skulls and bones."[113]

If the original practice of Bwiti did indeed involve human sacrifice or grave robbing, by the early twentieth century such archaic practices (if they had ever taken place) had long since been abandoned.[114] Later, ethnologists who spent time with the Fang people discovered that they were neither murderous savages nor grave robbers. In fact, the human bones they kept in wooden boxes belonged to their ancestors and were kept as shrines to respect and remember dead loved ones. Nevertheless, both the Catholic missionaries and the French Colonial governors (who believed Bwiti went hand in hand with civil disobedience) used such allegations and other trumped-up charges to justify the persecution of these defiant sorcerers.

Artworks and artifacts were either destroyed or seized, temples burned, and Bwiti clerics of both sexes shot as examples to others.[115] This led many to adopt Christianity, often for their own safety. However, in many cases, this oppression simply resulted in victims being extolled as martyrs and the shrouding of Bwiti practice in secrecy. Just like the European pagans of old, they hid their artifacts, concealed their activities, and held their ceremonies deep in the forests away from prying eyes.

Initially, ceremonies were practiced in secret by the Gabonese tribal Fang minority. Before long, Bwiti began to spread. Soon enough, its appeal had penetrated Cameroon, Zaire, Congo, Angola, and Equatorial Guinea. The practice even permeated the ranks of Government officials, including the Gabonese president himself. Moreover, its anti-colonialist beginnings helped galvanize the Gabonese national identity and played a notable role in creating a new Gabon republic that considered tribal values and lifeways a valued cultural asset.[116] Bwiti was hailed as an authentic celebration of what English explorer and ethnographer Mary Kingsley called "The African idea."[117]

MODERN(ISH) BWITI

If you ask the Bwiti to explain their tradition today, answers will vary according to the region they come from. The Tsogo people of Central and Southern Gabon may tell you they are the oldest Bwiti sect that exists. And that their Dissumba initiation ceremonies, which are based on ancestor worship and can last anywhere from a week to a month, most closely resemble those of their pygmy founding fathers.

In Central Gabon, the Missoko traditions practiced by the Mitsogo people include Ngonda (diagnosis), mioba (healing), singuedia (protection), maboundi (women), and bussouka (knowledge of creation). Although their ceremonies' intent is deadly serious, they may begin with a light party atmosphere and village get-together, whose rituals and energy sharply intensify as the night unfolds.

Much to Roman Catholics' ongoing dismay, some Bwiti sects have syncretized and absorbed Judeo-Christian mythologies, rituals, and liturgies into their practice. Moreover, the replacement of bread and wine with an ultra-powerful psychoactive root places the Bwiti concept of "communion" far beyond a symbolic platitude.

In the unlikely event one happened to stumble upon the secretive Fang Bwiti ceremonies of Southern Cameroon, you could be forgiven for thinking you'd wandered into a Catholic mass, complete with priests, nuns, artifacts, symbolism, hymns, church band, sermons, and liturgies. Only after receiving "communion," which does precisely what it says on the tin, do you realize that you're witnessing something very different. Soon thereafter, the gathering morphs into a frenzied display of live music, theater, symbolic rites, and an all-night dance marathon requiring the kind of stamina Olympic champions would kill for.

Although they differ in flavor, the various Bwiti traditions contain certain elements common to them all. The first element they share (urban practitioners notwithstanding) is lifeways that echo those practiced by humankind since our ancestors descended from the forest canopy; by hunting, gathering, and foraging throughout the jungles of west equatorial Africa.

To the western mind, a forest may conjure up images of a pleasant weekend hike, excursion, or camping trip. However, to the Bwiti, whose relationship with the natural world begins the moment they are born, the forest is a mother, a father, a giver of life, and a provider of everything required to sustain it. The jungle is an expansive egalitarian commune with more than enough resources to provide for the countless lifeforms it spawned, all of whom inherently understand how to live according to its rules. It is a medical cabinet, a grocery store, a caregiver, and a shelter provider.

Although some Bwiti villages engage in limited agriculture, trade and economic surplus are minimal. Many rely on the natural plant and animal resources available from their backyard, which is anything but minimal. To some, such means of acquiring food may seem antiquated and primal, that the menu is confined to the few tasteless plants fit for human consumption. They would be wrong. The Congolese rain forests are nothing less than a four million square kilometer organic supermarket, an abundant and eternal provider of the finest, healthiest superfoods on earth, all of which are free. Of course, you need to know where and how to look, which they most certainly do.

The second element Bwiti share is the conviction that true understanding of Bwiti can be achieved only through initiation. Until then, the secrets of Bwiti, which roughly translates to mean "dead," "deceased," or "ancestor," are essentially off-limits. The only way to understand Bwiti is to see Bwiti, and the only way to do that is to eat lots and lots of iboga.

In the words of Mme Nnoh, Bwiti practitioner and Secretary of Direction at CICIBA Libreville:

> "Bwiti is not a religion. It is neither a secret society. It is not even a sect. Bwiti is simply a tradition of our ancestors that everyone must know and

understand, particularly Africans. Prior to understanding this tradition, everybody must pass
through initiation rites."[118]

We learn from Nnoh's words that Bwiti is an ancestral tradition, but so is Christmas. The Bwiti themselves say that Bwiti
cannot be understood without an iboga-induced journey to
otherworldly realms. So now what? At this point, you may be
thinking, "we're going to need a little more to go on here." What
are these "initiation rites," and why are they the only thing that
offers a true understanding of Bwiti?

It's here that the majority of academic researchers slam
straight into a brick wall. Why? Because often, a researcher's
most commonly used information-gathering tool is literature.
The minuscule amounts of vague, albeit well-written attempts
to quantify the subject notwithstanding, very little of this material exists. Despite some notable attempts by visiting academics
to convey the lifestyle and practices of Bwiti into words on a
page, in truth, this is impossible.

Not only is Bwiti based around an edible, ultra-powerful
astral vehicle to ineffable realms, but it is also an oral tradition. This is precisely why it has avoided being constrained by
obscure ritualistic symbols or fallen victim to the ossified written creeds that bind other traditions. Except for what has been
recorded by a few intrepid Westerners, Bwiti has few written
teachings. After all, if the teachings come from a plant and are
different for everyone, why or how would they be recorded?
Why would one need clarification from a book when there's an
edible hotline to the source?

ACCESS DENIED

Okay, so the only way to acquire experience of Bwiti is to eat iboga, after which African initiates are famously tight-lipped about the nature of their adventures. But what about those intrepid Westerners? After entering rural Gabon, eating iboga, seeing and becoming Bwiti, and later emerging shell shocked from the jungle, what did they have to say about their experience?

One such adventurer is British indigenous rights campaigner, environmentalist, and award-winning documentarian, Bruce Parry. In 2005, the BBC aired six episodes of his documentary 'Tribe,' a series highlighting the environments, life-ways, and issues faced by some of the world's few remaining ancient tribes. Episode four chronicles Bruce Parry's trip to equatorial Gabon to undergo an iboga ceremony with the Babongo people.

The show opens with some historical and cultural information regarding Gabon, iboga, and what little is known of the Bwiti tradition. After spending a few days living with the Babongo tribe, it's time for Bruce to take the plunge. Night falls in the village. After ingesting iboga, Bruce reports feeling his *"blood on fire, growing panic, a rapid drop in blood pressure, and a momentary sensation that death is looming."*[119]

Just when things appear to be hotting up, the narrative is interrupted, and the camera crew is asked to quit filming. It's explained that the nature of the events about to take place is a strictly kept secret between Bruce and his Bwiti guide. Even with the camera turned off, the film crew is politely but firmly instructed to distance themselves from the proceedings. In a remote corner of Central Africa, it would seem even the BBC, one of the oldest and most prodigious media outlets in the world, can't snag a backstage pass to the show.

Today, the internet is awash with content, primarily written by Western providers who speak of Bwiti as a secret society, a mystical tradition, a healing system, and a visionary path of knowledge that links the visible and the invisible. It connects the higher dimensions with the terrestrial plains, offers an experiential lesson on the universe's workings, and much more. To the initiated, Bwiti may represent all of these, none of these, and countless elements in between.

In short, Bwiti is a mystery, wrapped up in a literal and pro-verbial enigma, a uniquely personal experience that no amount of purely academic searching can ever lead us to. In the absence of experience, Bwiti cosmology remains alien terrain, off-limits to modern Western thought paradigms. It includes ancient creation mythologies, animistic beliefs, alternative histories, primordial tales surrounding the fall of man, and the subsequent separation of heaven and earth, or the "dismemberment" between man and God.

Alan Watts, philosopher and poet-warrior extraordinaire, once wrote:

"many mythologies envisage the goal of life as the rememberment of the original dismemberment."[120]

Bwiti may be the ultimate example of the kind of mythology Watts was referring to, in which the modern humans' life purpose is nothing less than a recollection of the original "dismemberment." For all intents and purposes, this "dismemberment" is another name for the "social dislocation" psychologists identify as the root cause of the widespread existential despair that runs rife through western culture. It is this aspect of the iboga experience – this *recollection of the original dismemberment* that can act as a powerful beacon, shining in the dark, lovingly but firmly calling us back home after our 10,000 year-long, post-agricultural experiment with dislocation.

How does iboga do this? By showing us a glimpse of the long-forgotten physical and spiritual terrain upon which humankind evolved; the true Garden of Eden. Iboga is a time machine.

13

THE WAY BACK PLAYBACK

"Now he has departed from this strange world a little ahead of me. That means nothing. People like us, who believe in physics, know that the distinction between past, present, and future is only a stubbornly persistent illusion."[121]
Albert Einstein in a condolence letter to the family of Michele Angelo Besso.

Widely regarded as a Colossus of psychedelic chemistry, Nicholas Sand was revered in the psychedelic community for his pivotal role in the formation of alternative movements that emerged in the 1960s. In addition to producing mammoth quantities of weapons-grade LSD, Sand is also rumored to be the first underground chemist to have synthesized DMT.[122] Sand died in 2017, leaving a legacy and life story containing the stuff of any biography writer's dream. The following is an edited excerpt from a piece written by Sand in 1964, in which he recalls a vision witnessed during an iboga journey.

"After an immense journey, I came to a planet. Slowly, the planet cooled until fumes and vapors veiled the entire surface. As I circled the planet, I sensed a long epoch of torrential rains, as water vapor formed and condensed in the upper atmosphere and fell toward the burning surface, only to evaporate again long before reaching the ground. Eventually, the planet cooled and the rains arrived on the lands below. After what seemed like a long time, the clouds began to clear. I skimmed the planet now, seeing and being everything that I came across. I watched mountain chains rise and volcanoes burst, and everything subside again and again into flat plains and meandering rivers. Time and time again, mountains rose and dissolved and continents appeared and disappeared. Then this slowed down and I watched the seas and plains. All was sterile—a tan land with smoking volcanoes and no life, yet fecund and ready."

"As I watched, I then saw life appear. I observed spots of green forming along the seashores. They shot along the banks, forming a green margin and then running up the rivers and tributaries like the veins in a leaf. The barren spaces between these branches of life filled with proliferating plant life. The oceans seemed to be teeming with life and then the first bug-like creatures started to crawl out on land. They spread all over, rapidly changing into a variety of insects and strange lobster-like creatures."

"Fern-like plants appeared. Vast varieties of life appeared and then disappeared. Elaborate life experiments succeeded one another with awesome complexity."

"Then suddenly I was in a steaming swamp-like environment that looked familiar. With a sense of awe and amazement, I realized that I was watching the age of the dinosaur, and it slowly dawned on me that I was witness to the history of life evolving on the planet Earth! With a speed that defies accurate recall, life forms changed again and again, spreading and multiplying in a dizzying array of shapes and colors. Humanoid creatures appeared and soon after were hunting and then farming and building. Civilizations bloomed, spread, and subsided, like bubbles on a fermenting pond. Ages of war and conquest expressed the speed of civilization and technology. I witnessed slaughter and mayhem, torture and mutilation, rape and castration. Man's inhumanity to man was illustrated in myriad forms. I was there "in" it, feeling it as both the doer and the done to. For what seemed an interminably long time civilization rose and fell in inter-folding waves of creation and brilliant innovations in arts and sciences, only to fall in smoking ruins followed by ages of darkness."[123]

Suppose reports of this specific experience, featuring a visual recount of billions of years of evolution, were limited to Nicolas Sand and a few others. In that case, we could easily dismiss it. But this is not the case. Far from it. Nicolas Sand is simply echoing the same experience recalled by countless returning psychonauts.

Uncannily similar accounts of such visions described as *"the ultimate illustrated history lesson,"* during which one can witness *"the beginnings of the world,"* the *"birth and death of stars, and the formation of planets,"* resonate throughout countless recollections of psychedelic ceremonies.[124, 125]

Iboga is a powerful catalyst for this particular vision. How-ever, other compounds are known to provoke similar experi-ences. Anthropologist Reichel Dolmatoft reports that indig-enous users of Ayahuasca say the brew enables them to visit the place of creation, witness the act of creation, participate in the creation story, and comprehend the moral concepts it con-tains.[126] According to the Bwiti, this particular vision is experi-enced by those whose souls are as old or even much older than the earth. It is projected in order to convey the importance of caring for something that took billions of years to build.[127]

Witnesses to these phenomena (which does not include every-one) often consider it the most mind-boggling of all. While it may be natural for those unfamiliar with such an experience to raise an eyebrow, many individuals who have undergone an iboga ceremony understand that seeing is believing. It's also that we're talking about a psychoactive root that alludes to some of the strangest science known, or rather – unknown, to humankind.

In truth, this vision reflects one more component of the iboga experience that defies any attempt at 'rational' explana-tion. Even a 'rationally' minded reader hesitant to describe such notions as "mystical" may be forced to admit that such concepts knock loudly on the door of some deeply weird science. Cor-respondingly, the fields of transpersonal psychology, physics, and academic psychedelia have spawned some notable weird scientists, a few of whom have taken some commendable shots at interpreting the plant-induced time-travel phenomena.

INFINITY AND BEYOND

The only real research conducted on both the vision discussed herein and the obscure state of consciousness necessary to experience it comes not from iboga research but from those studying other potent psychedelic compounds known to provoke a similar encounter.

Benny Shanon is an Israeli cognitive psychologist. In his book *The Antipodes of the Mind,* Shanon reports that many ayahuasca users recall similar journeys back in time. Shanon writes:

> "some of the most spectacular visions that can be experienced are those interpreted as depicting the Creation of the universe," and "the creation of the world and the evolution of life."[128, 129]

Shanon is careful to avoid attributing such phenomena to the supernatural, instead proposing they are a product of the mind. Shanon argues that during the psychedelic journey, the brain areas that deal with time, notably the temporal lobe, begin to shut down. When the brain's temporal lobe ceases to function, our subjective grasp of time begins to dissipate, triggering experiences that demand a reevaluation of what "time" actually means.

None of the psychological literature, argues Shanon, can account for these extreme variations in one's experience of time, specifically when these temporal adjustments result in the experiencing of "eternity."[130, 131]

TIME IS A HUMAN CONSTRUCT

Yuval Harari points out that all non-human animals live in a field of limited consciousness. They understand objective entities that aren't themselves, such as prey, trees, rocks, and water. Any cognitive grasp of the subjective extends only to the feelings within themselves, such as fear, lust, and hunger.[131] There's no past and no future. There is only the present. To animals, the "power of now" isn't an abstract platitude. It's their everyday existence.

Around 70-100,000 years ago, one such animal underwent a neurological mutation that expanded its neocortex, providing them with an extra dimension of consciousness unique to their species. Bigger brains required larger skulls, creating dramatic changes in their jaws, tongues, lips, and voice box. Suddenly, this creature could use distinct, mission-specific sounds to convey concepts previously confined to their imaginations. Homo Erectus had become Homo Sapien – a brand new species that could walk, and above all, talk.

After realizing we could make cool words, we set merrily about slapping titles on everything around us, which at the time was primarily plants and animals. More importantly, we could convey information about things that don't actually exist: religions, nations, law, and other imaginary shared fictions that exist only in the mind and could only be imagined by a species capable of thinking in terms of past, present, and future.

For the human species, the cognitive revolution shattered the boundaries of the here-and-now. Our ability to live in the present shrank. Meanwhile, our egos grew, as did our creation of increasingly complex shared fictions. At the heart of it all lay two foundational fictions without which no others could have arisen—the concepts of subject vs. object (space) and past and future (time).

TIME IS AN ILLUSION

This chapter's epigraph contains an excerpt from a condolence letter written by Albert Einstein to the family of recently deceased Michele Angelo Besso, a Swiss/Italian engineer and Einstein's closest friend. Einstein writes:

"People like us, who believe in physics, know that
the distinction between past, present, and future is
only a stubbornly persistent illusion."[133]

So what happens when the 'persistent illusion' Einstein refers
to begins to dissolve, as recorded by psychologists, neurolo-
gists, and users of powerful psychoactive plant compounds?
When our temporal wall is temporarily demolished, what lies
on the other side?

"It's not just that one system drops away," says Robin Car-
hartt-Harris, *"but that an older system reemerges."* This far more
ancient system is primary consciousness, a cognitive state
where the ego relinquishes its grip and the unconscious *"is
brought into an observable space."*[134]

Could this be why newcomers to these plant traditions return
with descriptions like *"rebirth, reboot, reset, a reprogramming of
the psyche, a return to some primordial default mode of consciousness,"* and other verbal constructs that sound suspiciously close
to the mental processes of pre-cognitive revolution humans? Are
they attempting to describe in words a mode of non-duality consciousness that predates the existence of language?

Prior to the cognitive revolution, language as we know it did
not exist. Furthermore, neither did the temporal lobe (the area
of the brain that processes time), or the parietal lobe (which
processes our sense of space.) So, when people return from
these journeys gobsmacked, claiming that time and space
seemed to dissolve, do we attribute that to mysticism or God?
Or can it be chalked up to the genuine possibility that the plant
they ate temporarily shut down the neocortex, an area of the
brain that developed comparatively recently?

WHEN TIME STANDS STILL

"Tachypsychia" refers to a neurological condition whereby temporal perception, whether due to extreme awe, fear, bliss, or trauma, is drastically altered. Car crash survivors and other witnesses often describe this as a *"slowing down of time."*[135]

However, Shanon proposes that the psychedelic experience is not one of time passing more slowly but instead entering a state of being which is altogether outside the parameters and limitations of time.[136] Shanon argues that when we access mental realms that exist beyond past, present, and future, events that take place over centuries or millennia may be experienced in only moments of linear time.[137] This place has been named "the realm of the eternal." If that sounds weird, that's because it most definitely is, even after you've been there and seen it for yourself.

Essentially, "eternity" should not be confused with an infinitely long period of linear time. Instead, it is a place arrived at once time is transcended and thus ceases to exist.[138] Joseph Campbell describes eternity not as an earlier or later time, or even as a long time. Eternity, says Campbell, has nothing to do with time. Eternity is that dimension of here and now which thinking and time cuts out.[139]

STUMBLING INTO HEAVEN

In 1956, Stanislav Grof, a Czech-born psychiatrist, a leader in the field of transpersonal psychology, and pioneer of the holotropic breathing method, became one of the earliest subjects to undergo experimental testing of LSD-25. During his first session, Grof recalled being *"thrust into the middle of a cosmic drama that previously had been far beyond even my wildest imaginings.*"[140] During this consciousness shift, he experienced a tour of the universe, raced through black holes, witnessed the unfolding of the big bang and other cosmic wonders. In The Adventure of Self-discovery, Grof writes:

> "The subject can witness panoramic images of the evolution of the entire planet, including its origin as part of the solar system, the early geophysical processes, the situation in the primeval ocean, and the origin and evolution of life."[141]

He goes on to say:

> "The subject can witness or identify with the birth and development of the cosmos involving dimensions and energies of unimaginable scope. This can be various episodes from the cosmogenetic history of the Big Bang, the creation of matter, space, and time, the birth of galaxies and their expansion, explosions of novas and supernovas, and the contraction of large suns ending in black holes."[142]

After observing tens of thousands of subjects in altered states of consciousness, Stanislav Grof was left convinced that certain practices can bridge the gap between individual human consciousness and events that extend beyond our physical senses into history, nature, and the cosmos.

According to Grof, the leading explanation of why subjects recall witnessing the birth and evolution of the universe comes from Erwin Laszlo, a Hungarian quantum consciousness advocate, philosopher of science, and two-time Nobel Peace Prize nominee.[143, 144]

DOWN THE RABBIT HOLE

At this point, the science (no matter how weird) must make room for mysticism, conjecture, and an open mind.

ENTERING THE HOLOGRAPHIC UNIVERSE

In his written works, Erwin Laszlo postulated the existence of an extra-dimensional subquantum field, in which every single thing to have ever occurred in the history of our universe remains holographically recorded and stored.[145]

Oceans of ink have been spilled regarding the mind-boggling complexities of how Dennis Gabor, Karl Pribram, David Bohm, and others arrived at the Holographic Universe Theory. Their research is heavily rooted in relativity, consciousness research, quantum physics, interdimensional physics, and yes, that which may be loosely labeled "metaphysics." Their hypotheses touch upon the outer limits of the understanding of the world's sharpest scientific minds. Responses from the scientific community have ranged from skepticism to mystification. After reading Karl Pribram's work, award-winning quantum physicist Abner Shimony admitted, *"I'm afraid I just don't understand his theory."*[146] In contrast, heavyweight advocates include Nobel prize-winning professor of physics Brian Josephson, who stated that Bohm's work might someday provide the key to including consciousness, and even God within the scientific models.[147]

Detailed explanations of the holographic models are far beyond the scope of this book. Readers seeking to explore the Holographic Universe Theory will find the bibliography section contains some valuable suggestions. In the meantime, here is a radically shortened interpretation.

In 1947, Dennis Gabor, a British-Hungarian scientist, discovered that when two beams are projected onto a photographic plate, they create a stereoscopic three-dimensional image. Incredibly, it was revealed that every single piece of the image, however microscopic, contained the complete images data in its entirety. For example, if the glass that the image was projected onto were smashed into a million tiny pieces, each fragment would contain the object's total image. In Greek, the word "holos" means "whole," and "gramma" means "message." Thus, Gabor named his discovery the "Hologram," or "the whole message." Gabor's discovery changed the face of physics and landed him a Nobel prize

Hot on Gabor's heels, Karl Pribram, a psychologist and neurophysicist at Stanford University, was researching the brain's capacity to store memories. Pribram sought to understand why and how people remember things after certain parts of the brain had been destroyed by head injuries. To Pribram, the non-locality of holographic data storage looked like a solid candidate to explain cases where the patient's memory data remained intact despite the destruction of large areas of the brain. Pribram's subsequent Holonomic Brain Theory concluded that the human brain is a holographic storage unit in which memories are stored throughout the entire neural network and not in a single location as previously thought.[148]

Pribram needed support, which showed up in the form of David Bohm, a neuropsychologist, philosopher, and one of the most accomplished theoretical physicists of the twentieth century.[149] When presented with Pribram's Holographic Brain Theory, David Bohm took little convincing. Bohm's own studies had already led him to conclude that everything, every single unit of the cosmos from a speck of dust to the entire universe, and therefore the human brain, was a hologram.

Before the science of holography was discovered, Einstein wrote:

"A human being is part of the whole, called by us the 'universe,' a part limited in time and space. He experiences his thoughts and feelings as some-thing separate from the rest – a kind of optical delusion of his consciousness."[150]

At first glance, such a statement may sound like a new-age platitude. However, Einstein's statement is merely an extension of his general relativity theory, which posited time and space to be a sub-element of a larger space-time continuum. In David Bohm's eyes, the findings of Einstein merely scratched the sur-face. For Bohm, not just the human mind, not just space and time, but everything, every single thing to have ever existed in the history of the universe, from the nuclei of an atom to the entire universe itself, were seamlessly woven into one gigantic, unbroken continuum, in which everything exists in *every thing*. Just like a hologram.

Suppose Bohm and his scientific successors were correct? If so, does that mean that this book you now hold in your hand, along with the eyes you use to read with, and the part of the brain interpreting it and processing the letters into comprehen-sible data (AKA consciousness) are part of one single enormous chain in which nothing is separate?

ALL IN ALL

The idea that consciousness (immaterial) and solid objects (matter) are one and the same and that everything exists in *every thing* suggests something as basic as it is immeasurably complex. In the same way each fragment of a hologram contains the entire image, everything that exists in the universe, from the most minuscule of life's building blocks up, contains the entire universe itself. Let's suppose every cell in our body contains a holographic record of the entire history of life, earth, the cosmos, and the universe. If so, would that mean a recording of such must be present in a molecule of our saliva?

In an earlier chapter, it was written that during the "evaluative stage" of the journey *"iboga cracks open and scours one's memory bank."* But how far back, and for how long has the human *memory bank* been accepting deposits? In attempts to reconcile such visions, many claim that iboga seems to awaken millions of years of collective cellular memories stored deep within one's DNA. Considering human DNA has been proven to contain records of 4 billion years of encoded evolutionary history, such claims may not seem so far-fetched. If it does, then consider the raw power, and yes – data contained in the uranium-235 atoms deliberately collided over Hiroshima to devastating effect. Once we accept that such a minuscule object can easily accommodate such an enormity of content, the question then becomes merely one of accessibility. For Robert Oppenheimer et al., the answer was relatively simple: Divide the nuclear material into two sub-critical pieces and slam them together at high speed. Boom!

Obviously, unlocking the data concealed within one's own molecular structure requires a more subtle approach. To this end, could it be that nature devised and planted a far gentler technical solution right under our feet eons before scientists were aware atoms existed?

AS ABOVE SO BELOW. AS WITHIN SO WITHOUT

To clarify, let us refer back to Huxley's Mind-at-Large theory. When the "reducing valve" is operating as it should, the human perceptual radar is highly limited. Not only are our perceptual abilities constricted by the reducing valve, but by our physical body, our environment, space, and by time, which imposes a beginning and definitive ending on our physical bodies. This field is the microcosm. A convenient, albeit woefully inadequate way to think of the microcosm, is as the fractional selection of data from the physical world the brain deems fit to come aboard.

The macrocosm is then the sum total of all which eludes our waking perception—microwaves, radio waves, UV light, and so much more. From the tiniest elements that constitute matter, upwards to the entire universe and possibly beyond, and sideways through a potentially infinite range of interpenetrating dimensions that host the immaterial elements postulated by religion, mysticism, spirituality, and a "peak" psychedelic experience.

As the mystical experience of iboga takes hold, any perceived separation between the microcosm and macrocosm melts away, boundaries dissolve, and time becomes distorted. The 'I' ceases to exist. At this point, making clear-cut distinctions between where three-dimensional solidity intertwines with any number of alternate dimensions becomes a challenge. Once our hardwired preconceptions concerning the world of past and future (time) and matter (space) have dissipated, a chance emerges to witness any number of interpenetrating realities in holographic coexistence. Benny Shanon notes that from this eternal perspective, everything to have ever occurred, past, present, even future, is available for viewing.[151]

These transcendental domains have been given many names:

the dream space, the realm of archetypes, the collective uncon-scious, and the eternal in which oneself, the universe, and all else are one.

If that sounds way too 'hippy-dippy', consider that such expe-riences are just matter-of-fact to eastern mystics, particularly Buddhists or Taoists. Their traditions are based on a universe where the spiritual and the material cannot be divided and con-sider the experiencing of such to be the hallmark of the authen-tic mystical experience.

The only obstacle to experiencing this Divine oneness, Mind-at-Large, cosmic consciousness, Monad, holographic universe, God, or whichever label you choose, is the constrained percep-tual capacity of the human radar. Only when one's "Doors of Perception" stand ajar, ready to receive, does the line from the William Blake poem that inspired the title of Huxley's book begin to make sense:

> "If the doors of perception were cleansed every-thing would appear to man as it is, infinite."[152]

THE ULTIMATE HISTORY BOOK

Erwin Laszlo postulated that within these infinite realms is an extra-dimensional data-storage bank. Contained inside is the entire history of our universe, including our own physical and mental holograms. Although Laszlo's argument is rooted in hard science, he openly admits that such a hypothesis (that the roots of reality stem from a cosmic field that records and dis-penses information) smacks of mysticism and religion.

Laszlo's vision of applying modern science to ancient spir-itual beliefs is reflected in the title of his 2004 book *Science and The Akashic Field.* The idea of the "Akashic Records," "Akashic field," or the "A-Field," as Laszlo calls it, is a concept esoterically minded readers may already be familiar with. In Sanskrit, the word "Akasha" translates to "aether" or "atmosphere." The Hindu translation of "Akasha" means "heaven" or "sky." The term "Akashic records" (first coined by a nineteenth-century theosophist named Alfred Sinnet) was born from these concepts.[153]

In *Mysticism*, Evelyn Underhill describes this realm as the "cosmic memory," where the images of all events, including every human thought, utterance, intention, and emotion that ever occurred, are recorded and stored.[154]

Although imperceptible to standard human sensory apparatus, it has long been known that this realm is accessible either subconsciously through a near-death experience or dreaming, or consciously, via meditation, astral projection, and of course, psychoactive compounds.

Alice Anne Bailey was an English-born theosophist who wrote extensively on mystery school practices. In her book, *Light of the Soul on The Yoga Sutras of Patanjali,* she writes:

> "The Akashic record is like an immense photographic film, registering all the desires and earth experiences of our planet. Those who perceive it will see pictured therein the life experiences of every human being since time began."[155]

The holographic and Akashic models share strong similarities with Carl Jung's ideas concerning the "collective unconscious." In his famous 1916 essay, *The Structure of the Unconscious,* Jung refers to an;

"Unconscious hive mind shared by all of mankind, composed of basic representations of universal figures and relationships."[156]

Jung believed these "archetypes" to be a library of *primordial images* which act as the *"basic stock of the unconscious psyche."*[157] He believed humans were born with these elements imprinted on their subconscious mind and that they were drawn from the archaic psychic records of humankind's earliest ancestors. He also claimed that the collective unconscious realm they inhabited surpassed the human lifespan. Jung writes:

> "It is the mind of our unknown ancestors, their way of thinking and feeling, their way of experiencing life and the world, Gods and men. The existence of these archaic strata is presumably the source of man's belief in reincarnations and in memories of previous experiences. Just as the human body is a museum, so to speak, of its phylogenetic *[the study of the evolutionary history of organisms]* history, so too is the psyche."[158]

WHAT DOES THIS HAVE TO DO WITH IBOGA?

The preceding information is offered to outline some of the hypothetical explanations for the time-traveling visions experienced by Nicolas Sand and countless others. To date, there's no way to scientifically verify the Akashic records, Jung's archetypes, the Astral Plane, the Holographic Universe, or other fantastical realms to which iboga may grant access. This is heavy stuff for sure. Maybe this is why mainstream science is so quick to casually dismiss such things as far-flung, pseudo-scientific speculation.

Practically speaking, the elemental makeup, nature, and origins of these phenomena are irrelevant. They may come from other dimensions or realms. They may come from the brain. They may be esoteric or exoteric. Whether they be holograms, Akashic Records, God, complex neurochemical interactions, a collapse of the brain's Default Mode Network, a complex combination of the lot, or something completely different is a fascinating yet essentially moot question.

Beyond their naming, what remains is this: These realms can be experienced, and they are, under the right circumstances, eminently accessible. As such, the only real question left to the explorer is this: Which of the transpersonal vehicles required to journey to these domains will they choose?

Alice Bailey believed this terrain could be accessed through a variety of techniques. Echoing the warnings of occultist adepts throughout history, she insisted that the safest way to enter these realms was through disciplined practice. She believed that casually dropping in without the requisite navigational experience exposed one to confusion and falsehood. In the *Light of the Soul,* she writes:

> "Herein lies the great deception of the records. Only a trained occultist can distinguish between actual experience and those astral pictures created by imagination and keen desire."[159, 160]

Alice Bailey was opposed to using 'drugs' as a vehicle to gatecrash these domains, even going so far as to label such practices "black magic." Despite her opposition to the use of psychedelics, she acknowledges their effectiveness.

Alice Bailey was not the first to condemn these plant compounds as magic, black or otherwise. Although highly accomplished in her own right, it's doubtful that Bailey was familiar with either iboga, its powerful psychoactive counterparts, or the idea of responsible shamanism.

But what is "magic" anyway? The Vatican believed that magical compounds belonged in the infernal wastebasket of history, along with medicine, astronomy, herbalism, and other 'satanic' practices that would eventually become the bedrock of modern technology. As midwives (witches) were persecuted, mankind's earliest scientists risked their lives and liberty to decode the mysteries of matter through experimentation. For centuries, these alchemists, who defiantly regarded *"one man's magic to be another man's engineering,"* worked in the dark, spurred on by the conviction that anything magical was merely something waiting for mankind to crack the chemical combination lock.[161] As they progressed, the line between sorcery and science became increasingly blurred.

Fast forward a few centuries. The flying carpet became the helicopter, the elixir potions became penicillin, the wand became the rifle, and singular hand-written texts gave way to the printing press. The last example would serve as the conduit through which Arthur C. Clarke famously declared:

> "Any sufficiently advanced technology is indistinguishable from magic."[162]

Despite their inquiries, researchers have yet to unscramble how iboga achieves what it does. Considering such a quest may be the proverbial equivalent of trying to reverse engineer an alien spaceship or a time machine, is it any wonder such answers remain elusive?

Iboga is a technology whose mechanics surpass anything we currently know. Will we ever know? Or, is iboga simply a technology patiently awaiting the infant human intellects coming of age?

In the meantime, suppose we simply accept that iboga is a profoundly powerful cognitive tool designed and delivered to heal, bond, cleanse, awaken, trigger psychological upgrades, and accelerate humankind's evolutionary curve. If we can do this, do we even need to rush to understand how such technology works?

Among many other things, iboga is a self-driving spaceship that (if it believes the passenger is suited) can take them anywhere and everywhere. Trips can even include a spectacular visionary tour that kicks off at the birth of the universe and ends at the present day. This is not speculation. This is a plain fact that has been documented and recalled by Western users, Bwitists, and users of other powerful psychedelics.

The question then arises: what purpose does the time-traveling aspect of this natural technology serve?

14

IF SO, SO WHAT?

"The human ideal then, becomes the sage, or;
'divine man' whose consciousness transcends the
opposites and who, therefore, knows himself to be
one with the cosmos. We conclude with visions of
the universe seen from this point of view."[163]

Alan Watts

fter Nicholas Sand's iboga journey through space and
time, he concluded as follows:

"As I lived through this flux and change, there
arose in me an awareness of the noble and brave
potential of humanity and its duty as the intelligent species to protect the forests and life forms
and water of the planet. I was experiencing a feeling of the sacred unity with all life. I saw the whole
planet's surface as one organism inhabited by one
spirit growing its forests to protect its surface and
provide even moisture and temperature for all its
creatures. I saw one species, humanity, as the natural intelligent guardian of all life. I realized that it
was humanity's intelligence that must understand,

preserve, and care for the earth's surface—and life that is its nutrient substrate, its womb, and its mother. I felt how all life was precious, interconnecting, and supportive of all other life. I dedicated my spirit not to destroy any part of this puzzle of divine mystery that is the milk of creation."[164]

RETURN TO INNOCENCE

The baptism of the soul bestowed by iboga has been expressed as a glimpsing return to innocence, Eden, the source, eternity, or an infinite and eternal reservoir of primordial wisdom wherein lies a snapshot of original, pre-cognitive revolution, non-duality consciousness.

How fitting that a root that grows in a location suspected to be the cradle of humankind and dates back far older than we can imagine has the power to transport us back to our evolutionary, cultural, psychological, and physiological roots. After thousands of years of pedal-to-the-metal materialism, evolutionary disinformation, and psychological carpet bombing, it seems iboga is trying to reawaken humankind from mass cultural amnesia, and in so doing, reconnect us with a past from which we were severed.

After a lifetime of assault from the media, cultural programming, religion, Coca-Cola, GMOs, celebrity, war, twisted histories, and decades of spiritual, emotional, cultural, and physical toxins, many claim iboga acts to blow the dust off the primordial hardcode engraved upon us at the start, and simply remember.

"All learning is remembering," said Plato, who believed the purpose of the psychedelic Eleusinian mysteries was to lead us back to the principles from which we descended.[165]

Which "principles" was Plato referring to? Was he suggesting iboga and other compounds would immediately make us see the error of our ways and spark a collective return to the hunter-gatherer, foraging ways of the stone age? Highly unlikely, and even if so, entirely unrealistic.

Daniel Quinn reminds us that any modern investigation into these *"principles from which we descended"* need look no further than the few remaining hunter-gatherer cultures.

According to Quinn, these groups never forgot that;

> "we are a biological species in a community of biological species and are not exempt or exemptible from the forces that shape all life on this planet."[166]

Whether Quinn knew it or not, his perspective is virtually indistinguishable from shamanism, which Terence Mckenna describes as;

> "not simply a collection of elaborate rituals, ordeals, and pathological personalities, at its fullest shamanism is a dynamic connection into the totality of life on the planet."[167]

In *Archaic Techniques of Ecstasy,* Mircea Eliade writes;

> "the goal of many shamanistic tribes is to restore the road between heaven and earth as it was established by the Creation. By doing so, they, in a manner abolish the present fallen state of the universe and humanity and re-establish the primordial situation, when heaven was easily accessible to all men."[168]

To the Bwiti, experiencing this "primordial situation" in our personal or collective history and subsequently integrating the teachings into one's life lies at the heart of both the healing process and the initiation into the Bwiti tradition.[169, 170] Essentially, these plant technologies work by reminding them of the world from which we came. By temporarily taking us back, they often succeed in taking us permanently forward.

In the movie *Back To The Future* Marty McFly climbs through the gullwing doors of his DeLorean car, keys in the desired date, and away he goes. Some iboga time-travelers report a similar concept. In fact, there's not even a need to type. Like the mythical UFOs purportedly behind the locked doors of clandestine Government cells, this vehicle can be operated on thought alone. Or at least a polite request. Alternatively, iboga may take control and select a destination that suits the needs of the subject.

To the therapy seeker, the experience may be understood as a regression to the source of their traumas. After facing down their pain, it lessens its hold on them and helps to reframe their perspective.

Similarly, the heroin user may experience a visionary return journey to the birth of their woes. Practically speaking, they may also undergo a reset of the opiate receptors to a neutral, opioid intolerant state.

For those seeking spiritual alignment or searching for an increased sense of purpose in the modern world, the experience may include front row tickets to the creation and evolution of the universe and planet earth. Just as Abraham Maslow insisted that the most efficient route to self-actualization was to find meaning via the "peak experience," this reconnection with the mythological past and restored understanding that the microcosm and macrocosm are inseparable is central to Bwiti's message of hope and personal transformation.[171]

Regardless of how this journey unfolds, Bwiti members know all about the power of these plants to transport one in time. It matters not whether that history is personal or shared, modern or ancient, literal or figurative. On a symbolic level, it is a form of "historical sorcery" that restores people to a primordial condition of identification with the cosmos and reconnects and realigns them with the natural world.[172, 173]

This experience can sometimes (but not always) be unsettling. Nevertheless, it returns us polished, ready, and with a newfound certainty which (even upon realizing the magnitude of the challenge) empowers us to step back into the world with confidence and purpose. As Joseph Campbell observed, it shows us:

> "that this horror is simply the foreground of a wonder and to come back and participate in it."[174]

Among other things, it achieves this by ascribing the individual a new, personal mythological anchor point, essentially replacing the stories they once told themselves about themselves with a far more meaningful call to action. Arguably, iboga may rank as the most powerful medium of this message. However, it is not the only psychoactive plant compound eager to emphasize the urgency with which we need to get our house in order. For those who have bared witness, the message is as candid as can be:

> "Get off the fence, or get off the planet!"

For some, this stark new perspective may mean renouncing activities that fuel the problem, ranging from meat-eating to trading their car for a bicycle. Others often find themselves called to increase their personal or civic involvement in conservation, animal welfare, or other causes. For others, this

newfound clarity concerning planetary abuse, pollution, species extinction, and deforestation moves them to redirect and
even dump their careers to become environmental lawyers,
field biologists, or organic farmers.[175]

Again, as crazy as it may sound to the uninitiated, this phenomenon is nothing new to shamanistic cultures, particularly
the Bwiti.[176] The same shift in perspective has been recorded by
countless westerners while undergoing the iboga journey. Dumb-
struck with wonderment newcomers to these traditions may be.
But, in fact, they've simply been exposed to a truth that slowly
but surely began to dissolve from western thought after the agricultural revolution – a truth which many shamanistic cultures
never forgot. Within such cultures, the shaman is revered as an
ecological guardian whose role is to mediate between the people
and their environment by engaging in dialogue with nature.[177]
The time to reopen this dialogue is yesterday.

Among other things, iboga is a communication technology.
We may define that as we wish: A bridge to restore harmony
between the natural domains, a telepathic WhatsApp message
carrying a blueprint for the next generation of environmental
science, or an ancient hard drive containing a registry of the
biosphere's complex information exchange.[178]

How about a desperately needed turbo injection capable of
jump-starting humankind's mental and spiritual evolution with
the force and speed required to stabilize and then reverse the
health crisis faced by our ecosystems and our species?

Maybe the greatest irony is that while modern tech titans
consider artificial intelligence to be the technological holy grail,
the intelligence they seek may be growing right under their feet.
Regardless of labels, the plant technology utilized by these "primitives" surpasses anything a modern tech genius, neuroscientist,
physicist, chemist, or religious guru can yet comprehend.

15

CONCLUSION

"History is the story of our unfocused agony over the loss of this perfect human world, and then of our forgetting it altogether, denying it and in so doing, denying a part of ourselves. It is a story of relationships, quasi-symbiotic compacts, with plants that were made and broken. The consequence of not seeing ourselves as a part of the green engine of vegetable nature is the alienation and despair that surrounds us and threatens to make the future unbearable."[179]

Terence Mckenna

In 2015, economists Angus Deaton and Anne Case noted that between 1999 and 2013, the mortality rate of white, middle-aged, working-class Americans went through the roof. This twenty-two percent increase in premature deaths was fueled by a tsunami of opioid overdoses, alcohol-related fatalities, and suicides. Deaton and Case cited declining wages, marital failure, dwindling job satisfaction, lack of social cohesion, and perhaps, racial privilege as the driving forces of this phenomenon. Although they offer no single definitive cause for these incidents, they identify the overall culprit as a sweeping cultural sense of meaninglessness, hopelessness, and despair rooted in the winner-takes-all socio-economic climate of modern-day North America.[180]

Anxiety, PTSD, alienation, meaninglessness, dislocation from nature, and existential angst are at an all-time high in western culture. Consequently, so is addiction. Meaning, humanness, purpose, spirituality, reverence for the natural world, and yes – 'religion' are no longer the "opiate of the masses." Now, the opiate of the masses is opium.

Is it not fascinating that compounds known to help address such things have made landfall during such a pivotal moment in western history? Is it pure coincidence? Is it a simple case of supply and demand? Or is it down to another mysterious force that knows a successful ambush is all about timing? As Evelyn Hill wrote:

> "It is significant that many of these experiences are reported to us from periods of war and distress: that the stronger the forces of destruction appeared, the more intense grew the spiritual vision which opposed them."[181]

When these *"forces of destruction"* first set foot in West Africa, the target was lumber and slaves. The social links formed during their enslavement would spark iboga's spread from the deepest jungle interior to the larger community. As for the lumber, demand is now greater than ever. So is the hunger for copper, diamonds, gold, uranium, cobalt, and oil that lie in abundance beneath the Congo basin's mineral-rich soil.

The forces of destruction at work in equatorial Africa's jungles are the same as in the Amazon and other ancient home territories to these natural medicines. It seems almost like these plants have acknowledged they can't win the war on their home-front and responded by lobbing a high-tech, neurochemical grenade deep behind enemy lines, smack bang in the heart of the occupier's homeland, hoping their message will go viral.

When something shows up with the potential to help addiction or addictions' precursive sense of social dislocation, it's little wonder this compound's perfectly timed arrival makes the mega-rich heroin dealers begin to sweat. Considering some of these pharmaceutical megalopolies were built on opioids, is it any wonder they get nervous?

Yet still, opportunity knocks. In response to the public backlash, growing fury, and ongoing gazillion-dollar class-action lawsuits, companies who derived much of their wealth from the opioid crisis are locked in an ultra-competitive scramble to profit from the cure. However, while greed, profit, and a mindset of dominance at all costs remain the key motivations, the shamanic knowledge of altered modes of consciousness, and the associated addiction-beating sense of meaning these plant experiences bestow will remain impossibly out of their reach.

While big-pharma, along with biotech companies working to strip Tabernanthe Iboga of its hallucinogenic properties are missing the point, the rest of the world is catching on. Until recently, these plants' power to fundamentally change one's consciousness for the better was an individual-level awakening. Nowadays, it is a collective mass movement that grows daily in volume and conviction. Vocal proponents of practices once demonized as the domain of hippies, slackers, and even sorcerers now include physicists, doctors, psychologists, and entrepreneurial titans.

Spearheading this brave new world is the sweeping realization that certain plants offer the power to restore one's sense of wonder, resuscitate reverence for nature, and empower one to get one's act together. Additionally, they offer a massively enhanced understanding of the relationship between psychology and human spirituality in all its infinite forms. The dawning awareness that these compounds may, as crazy as it sounds, represent real hope for humanity's future is precisely why they are now poised to come of age and reclaim their rightful position as a birthright of our species.

The Next Cognitive Revolution

The seeds have been sown. The thought revolution has begun. It is only a matter of time before history shows how crazy it was that these compounds were outlawed in an era when demand for psychological wellness far eclipses supply. Around the globe, people are reaching the long-overdue conclusion that one of the only things capable of addressing deep spiritual injuries is profound spiritual medicine. Meanwhile, perfectly functional, injury-free individuals are realizing that these compounds are not just for the sick or the addicted. They stand ready to meet and serve all of us, no matter whether we stand on top-of-the-world or at death's door. (As to the latter, don't we all)?

In a world crying out for a sense of meaning, or a mythology that makes sense, is it any mystery why so many young people have jumped on the psychedelic tourism bandwagon rolling through the jungles and pueblos of Amazonia, and slowly but steadily the rain forests of western equatorial Africa? What brings these westerners to endure slumming it in the wilderness simply to partake in a serious hallucinogenic ordeal that shows them their mortality and very possibly the darkest corners of one's soul?

Critics of this grass-roots movement often deride it as little more than an exotic quest into the extraordinary in search of

Instagram oneupmanship. This is certainly the case for some. However, for so many more, this shallow assessment fails to account for the growing numbers of intelligent, increasingly anxious young individuals with the conviction to move beyond their comfort zone in search of healing, self-reflection, and a sense of purpose. To find this, they must go in search of a cultural and mystical experience that is absent from and usually illegal within their home countries. These individuals are waking to the idea that these supposedly archaic traditions are a keystone component of the building materials required to repair the fractured world handed to them as their inheritance.

Just because this healing and reparation goal is on the horizon does not necessarily ensure the road will be smooth. Amid the hype, we should remember that these plants are powerful, immediate psychological game-changers, meaning while they represent a solution for many, they are not suitable for everyone. Once the guidelines for their use have been set, mainstream western acceptance will require legal U-turns, courage, determination, patience, compassion, understanding, and humility. Crucially, it will require penitence on behalf of Governments and institutions that for so long dismissed native cultures that use and understand these plants as 'archaic' and 'primitive.'

Difficult though this challenge may be, the prize of rekindling the plant partnership divorced from western culture for far too long is a temporary but profound liaison with the most beautiful of mysteries. Here, one is reminded of a consciousness symbolized in the ancestral playground of our ancient childhood. It returns us reset, rebooted, and with a rich, robust personal mythology - a new story to tell ourselves about ourselves, about the world around us, and how best to engage it during this perplexing game called "life."

In this book's opening passages, you may recall iboga being mentioned as a potential candidate for the mythological tree of knowledge mentioned in the Genesis story. Maybe it was. Perhaps it was not. Either way, it's no coincidence that the Genesis tale speaks of another tree. This tree teaches that life's meaning is not found in death, or near-death experiences, or veiled, mysterious realms, but in the here and now, by living as fully and creatively as humanly possible. This is the tree of life; the tree humankind supposedly waved goodbye when embarking upon our journey into dualistic thought. This is the tree to which we need to return. It is the tree to which many claim iboga implores us to return.

Among the varied messages iboga wishes to convey, maybe, what the plant is saying can be surmised thus:

> "You're welcome for the taste. So happy I could heal and educate you, and thanks for the visit. Oh, and, if you expected to be the same person you were before, then prepare to be joyfully mistaken. It's time to return from this magical place, and apply the received insights towards healing, dancing, singing, creating wonderment, and authoring some brand new stories. You are blessed with higher talents. Use them. Roll up your sleeves, reenter the world as caretakers, and begin reclaiming the planet as the equal domain of all living things. Good luck and Godspeed!"

Such is the power of iboga. It is the root of a primordial tradition, the root of remembrance, the root of existential reflection, the root of revelation, the root of awakening, and the root of self-authored sovereignty. Above all, it is the root of healing.

Approach it with reverence, intention, gratitude, and an open heart and mind, and you may return possessed of a gift unlike any other. It is the gift of meaning, and by extension, an understanding of what a gift it is to be a co-author in the human story.

THE END(ISH)

IV

ADDITIONAL INFORMATION

16

THE MONEY TREE: IBOGA SUSTAINABILITY AND CONSERVATION

Between 2001 and 2006, it was reported that the use of ibogaine in addiction treatment increased four-fold.[182] Since this data was released, it's logical to assume that the popularity of ibogaine has continued to rise. If further evidence is needed, one need only browse the internet to see how many new treatment facilities have appeared in the last decade. Although this may come as good news for addicts, the proliferation in therapy providers is not without drawbacks. Notably, the pressures it has reportedly wrought on populations of wild iboga plants in Central Africa. If reports are to be believed, iboga's new-found fame has been a blight on both the plant itself and the people for whom it remains a mainstay of their tradition.

Like tiger parts, as demand rises and supply dwindles, iboga becomes a more lucrative and desirable commodity than ever before. Unlike tiger parts, or rhinoceros horn, or pangolin blood, whereby purported medical benefits are rooted in falsehoods and primitive quackery, iboga's most significant threat may be that it actually works. Some members of the iboga community perceive the plant's outlawed status in certain countries to be its chief savior. Right or wrong, they argue that mainstream acceptance of iboga for healing, spiritual development, or addiction would make the plant's extinction inevitable.

It would be wrong to suggest the transformational role iboga has played in the lives of so many is anything less than an incredibly positive thing. However, when a revered, highly localized medicinal sacrament is increasingly regarded as an economic commodity to be plundered, packaged, auctioned off, and eventually consumed by a relatively privileged, predominantly Caucasian demographic, it's easy to understand the frustration felt by some of these native groups. Many have stated they welcome iboga's entry into the west. To others, iboga's meteoric rise in demand means their doorway to the divine, which stood open upon request since time immemorial, is now closing.

The scarcity of reliable data surrounding existing wild stocks, harvesting techniques, true market growth, and more make clearcut statements concerning iboga's current conservation status difficult to make. While one Bwiti member may tell you wild iboga is becoming scarce, another may laugh, claiming it grows everywhere. Arriving at any definitive conclusions will require increased efforts to survey and surmise a range of contributing factors.

Nevertheless, just because definitive conclusions remain elusive in no way indicates that what little research data exists should be dismissed, particularly when supported by substantial anecdotal evidence suggesting the Tabernanthe Iboga plant may be under threat.

In 2004, a French native named Yann Guignon was introduced to iboga by a traditional Gabonese healer. Two years later, his chemical addictions gone, Guignon went to Gabon to partake in a Bwiti Dissumba initiation with the ethnic Fang group. This event marked the beginning of a deep cross-cultural relationship to which only a handful of westerners had ever been privy. Guignon trained as a Kambo (Temple Guardian) and became deeply immersed in the study and practice of the Gabonese forest dwellers' life-ways.

Sometime later, Guignon teamed up with Professor Jean-Noel Gassita P.hD, a Gabonian presidential advisor and one of the world's leading authorities on ibogaine. United in their concern for dwindling wild Tabernanthe Iboga stocks, Guignon and Gassita embarked on a government-commissioned fact-finding mission. Guignon's field data, Gassita's research findings, and input from Bwiti representatives combined to confirm what many had long suspected.

In 2012, Guignon submitted a 50-page report to the Gabonese government. The report suggested that Tabernanthe Iboga plants were disappearing from the Gabonese rain forests and even went so far as to state without urgent measures to protect this precious natural resource, iboga could disappear in the wild.[183]

By 2014, Guignon had been appointed as a benefactor of Gabon's cultural heritage. In a keynote speech at the Global Ibogaine Therapy Alliance's (GITA) international conference in Durban, he expanded on the key dangers faced by wild iboga. Guignon outlined seven key factors contributing to the plant's demise.

INCREASING GLOBAL DEMAND

This is by far the leading culprit behind iboga's reported decline. In response, the spotlight has shifted to the Voacanga Africana tree. This tree is already cultivated in other parts of Africa. It contains the voacangine alkaloid, which can be semi-synthetically converted into pure ibogaine hydrochloride (HCL) in a cost-effective manner. It would be nice to think all ibogaine clinic operators remain conscientious about where their ibogaine is sourced and only use ibogaine harvested from the Voacanga Africana tree. Whether this is the case is difficult to ascertain.

Outside of clinical settings, demand for iboga from individuals happy to ignore the risks and administer it to themselves privately has also increased. In a marketplace this lucrative, root bark prices have shot up between 8-10 times that of a decade ago, placing root bark beyond the reach of many traditional practitioners.

EVANGELICAL INFLUENCE

It's been more than a century since the first catholic missionaries set foot in Gabon. Despite examples of Bwiti practitioners integrating the Christian faith into their belief systems, catholic missionaries continue to condemn the use of iboga and vilify its practitioners. Over time, catholic missionary influence has succeeded in drawing people away from traditional practices. Furthermore, this influence has permeated Gabonese politics, making the generation of financial support for preservation programs increasingly tricky.

CLIMATE CHANGE

Many regions of Africa have spent decades living under the looming shadow of climate-related risk and uncertainty. Few areas of the continent are more threatened by climate change than Sub-Saharan Africa. Specifically, countries in and around the Congo Basin. Increased temperatures have already resulted in shorter rainy seasons, placing greater stress on the entire Congo basin rain forest ecosystem.

The second-largest tropical rain forest on earth after the Amazon basin, the Congo basin is often referred to as the planet's "second lung." Compared to the existential threat faced by this critical component of the global ecosystem, issues surrounding the pressures on iboga may sadly seem trivial.

DEFORESTATION

Like the Amazon, the old-growth rain forest of the Congo is a treasure trove of natural resources. Along with a wide-ranging pharmacopeia of plants prized for their edible and medicinal properties, the Congo Basin is a massive repository of timber cobalt, oil, and more. The demand for these minerals has resulted in massive deforestation. Despite the Gabonese government declaring 17% of the nation's landmass protected, deforestation and the continued plunder of natural resources remain a continued threat to Tabernanthe Iboga's natural habitat.

URBANIZATION

In 1982, James Fernandez wrote in his seminal Bwiti ethnography that iboga and its associated spiritual practices played a significant role in maintaining the relationship between the forest peoples and their environment. These traditional practices caused many forest dwellers to eschew leaving for the towns and cities in favor of remaining in their villages.

Fernandez's book was published nearly four decades ago, at a time when a mere 20% of the Gabonese population was urban. Today, an estimated 85-90% of the Gabonese people live in towns and cities. Accelerated urban sprawl has further encroached on the rain forest environment, and many have chosen to disassociate themselves from traditional practices.

LACK OF AGRICULTURAL KNOW-HOW

The Congolese inhabitants of the bio-region in which Tabernanthe Iboga grows are among the last remaining true hunter-gatherer cultures on the planet. Although small quantities of iboga have been cultivated in villages, their limited understanding of agricultural techniques makes this difficult.

ANIMALS

The life cycle of Tabernanthe Iboga is intrinsically connected to the animals that eat its fruit. Chief among these creatures are elephants, who then redistribute the iboga seeds throughout the Congo Basin. Consequently, iboga plants are often found growing near well-worn elephant trails. This lucrative opportunity didn't go unnoticed by elephant poachers supplying ivory to the traditional Chinese medical market.

According to the report, the same individuals implicated in the ivory trade are also well-known black market iboga traders. The top of the ivory trade chain is home to international organized crime syndicates that fund and arm African militant extremist groups. These militant radicals arm and protect elephant poachers, creating a devastating feedback loop that ripples far beyond the Congo Basin.

At the time of writing, it's been nearly a decade since Yann Guignon brought his case to the Gabonese authorities, paving the way for legal measures designed to protect wild stocks of Tabernanthe Iboga. United by the conviction that iboga's extinction in the wild would constitute a colossal and irreparable deficit to humanity, a growing number of passionate individuals began proactively working to address the situation. Their laudable efforts towards sustainability are already starting to bear fruit.

After reading the report, President Ali Bongo integrated Tabernanthe Iboga into the Nagoya Protocol, an international treaty created to protect the "genetic resources" of each of the 93 signatory nations. This provided the first binding legal framework for safeguarding both the plant and the traditional knowledge associated with it.

This was a good start. However, many thought it didn't go far enough. Accordingly, a handful of NGOs, including Yann Guignon's *Blessings of the Forest*, began programs to encourage sustainable cultivation of iboga. Other local institutions began creating sustainable iboga plantations. Additionally, the Global Ibogaine Therapy Alliance (GITA) began working remotely and locally alongside volunteers to establish microfinance lending programs aimed at creating sustainable plantations in Cameroon and eventually beyond.

In February 2019, Tabernanthe Iboga's protections increased when Gabonese authorities decreed that without special export authorization from the government, the export of any part of the plant, including its derivatives, was illegal.

Outside of the Congo Basin, whispers surrounding the existence of Tabernanthe Iboga farms are based largely on hearsay. However, there also exists a limited number of verified Tabernanthe Iboga cultivation sites showing early signs of success.

Many of these farms are run by small teams of dedicated individuals located in Central America. This includes Mexico, Costa Rica, and beyond, where the latitude and fertile environment necessary to raise this delicate plant qualifies them as suitable alternative locations.

As far as the author is aware, these farming endeavors remain in their infancy. Additionally, the coming-of-age period of iboga's psychedelic alkaloids may be anywhere between 5-10 years, meaning it may be some time before reliable data surrounding these programs' success emerges. In the interim, these growers are working diligently and with cautious optimism to ascertain whether Tabernanthe Iboga plants can reach harvestability outside of their native habitat. At this stage, the future of such programs looks promising.

The technical aspects of iboga cultivation are outside the scope of this book. Anyone interested in cultivating iboga in a country where such activities remain unlegislated may find the internet the best place to start. Here, you can find several online discussion boards, grower forums, along with a few rough guides to the cultivation process.

17

THE LIFE COACH: MICRODOSING WITH IBOGA

Bwiti members, some of whom microdose daily and all of whom do so during ceremonies, understand that microdosing with iboga offers an effective way to work with the plant without having to undergo the rigorous demands of a flood dose. If used mindfully, it can act as a powerful ally to those seeking mental clarity, inner peace, and a sense of direction. In the same way LSD has been shown to provide answers to scholarly dilemmas, a low-dose regimen of iboga can deliver technical solutions for the soul. It is gentle, effective, and has the power to affect change. That said, everyone's microdosing experience will be different. Although many report benefits, a few may find working with iboga is just not for them.

Before delving further into iboga's microdosing potential, there are a few issues that need raising. The following information is given to highlight some of the more prominent physiological and ethical issues surrounding iboga microdosing.

Meticulous medical screening is the hallmark of any responsible iboga provider. Whether this applies to anyone thinking of adopting a personal, unsupervised microdosing regimen is less straightforward. One thing not up for dispute is this: Should one choose to microdose, then mistaking the super-concentrated ibogaine HCL you bought from the internet for root bark may be a risky affair. You may read verified accounts of addicts receiving boosters or test doses of ibogaine HCL in low doses. In all likelihood, these doses are weighed to the microgram and administered to pre-screened patients by trained professionals.

The remaining choices are either root bark or its total alkaloid extract, which raises issues of sustainability and legality. The ibogaine alkaloid can be extracted from other sources, namely, the Voacanga Africana tree. This is not the case for root bark or TA extract, which comes solely from the Tabernanthe Iboga plant. If you seek either of these preparations, do everything to ensure that, if sourced from Gabon, legal protocols have been followed. This applies equally to those planning to undergo a flood dose. If mental health and well-being come at the expense of the Bwiti culture and the dwindling Gabonian rain forests they call home, then maybe think about seeking alternative options.

It should also be remembered that some samples of iboga purchased online have been found to be old, moldy, and in some cases, different compounds entirely. Although many say online trades have gone smoothly, others report being either outrightly swindled, or receiving a product of dubious quality.

Finally, anyone thinking of microdosing iboga should remain aware of two things.

1. Iboga does not mix well with other substances. Alcohol, antidepressants, SSRIs, and other medications should be avoided before you proceed. The cleaner you are, the better the results will be. As such, yoga, meditation, good dietary choices, or any other practice that promotes physical alignment and mental clarity can be effective supplements when working with iboga.

2. The unspoken truth on the matter is that yes; microdosing iboga can be a good way to kick back and enjoy its antidepressant or mood enhancing effects. However, if that's one's goal, substances exist that are cheaper, more available, and more suitable than iboga. Iboga is a master medicine of unfathomable power. Traditionally, it is taken with reverence, respect, and humility. Many would argue it should be used for the right reasons, accompanied by solid intent, and offset by positive affirmations. Used in this manner, it may bestow profound insights and target problem areas that users were unaware existed until they began working with the plant.

THE ULTIMATE LIFE COACH

After ingesting low doses, users say that the spirit of iboga manifests as a gentle yet authoritative voice offering concise guidance in the supervision of one's own psyche. Similar to the result of meditation, it promotes a mode of thinking usually eclipsed by the onslaught of opposing inner voices clamoring to be nominated chief-adviser. Or, as Aldous Huxley described it, *"that interfering neurotic who, in waking hours, tries to run the show."*[184]

Microdosing iboga temporarily liberates the subject from the daily game of psychological whack-a-mole played out in order to make it through the day. Hardwired negative thought patterns, long since burnt into the neural pathways, are banished to the back seat to be replaced by gentle, firm utterances concerning the best way to proceed. The Bwiti call this *"the voice of truth."*

THE POWER OF NOW

It's common knowledge that iboga's strength-giving properties were recognized and subsequently banned by the International Olympic Committee. What was not recognized is iboga's ability to fortify the mind and direct one's thought patterns down a singular express lane.

Japanese martial artists refer to it as "mushin," sports psychologists as "the zone"; a rare, elusive operating condition where fear and other negative thoughts are denied entry. Instead, they are replaced by a state of increased mental function that facilitates an otherwise impossible fluidity of precise physical movement. It is a state in which extreme mindfulness has given way to "flow." Steven Kotler, the co-founder of the Flow Genome Project, says:

> "In flow, we are so focused on the task at hand that everything else falls away. Action and awareness merge. Time flies. Self vanishes. Performance goes through the roof."[185]

Like LSD and psilocybin, many who microdose iboga claim the lag time between thought and action is so quick that the intention doesn't even seem to register, instead acting on an immediate, primal instinct. The martial artist may see the punch seconds before it is thrown. A vastly increased reflex time may allow the surfer to read the wave far in advance, and respond with a cutback of previously unmanageable precision. The Bwiti say this iboga-induced tunnel vision makes them more efficient hunters.

The list goes on. From the triathlete to the artist to the heroin addict, iboga manifests not necessarily as a voice telling them what they "can" do, but as a mental editor, denying the negative narratives a ticket aboard one's thought train. Long after the iboga has worn off, this broadened perspective on personal potential remains, acting to remind and guide future performance.

The moment the plant enters one's system, people report it begins toiling to liberate the internal guru long buried by a lifetime's worth of stale information and outdated emotions. This build-up of psychological debris often stands as an insurmountable obstacle standing between who you are and who you have the power to become. Enter iboga's microscopic cleaning crew of nano-technicians, who diligently begin scrubbing away the cognitive rubble and clearing a path to right-mindedness.

The resulting thought patterns have been described as clean, clear, and irrefutably on the lookout for one's best interests. It shows the user that while the mind can be a powerful practical tool, it will, given a chance, render them a slave to their thoughts. It provides a powerful lesson in the kind of thinking that can be achieved when one learns to filter out the background noise, muzzle the negative self-reviews, and connect with the heart. These actions may continue to serve as a road map to personal success long after iboga has left the system. Once again, it changes the stories we tell ourselves about ourselves, thus vastly increasing our notion of what the mind and body are truly capable of and not what the mental quitter would have us believe.

18

THE PHYSICIAN: IBOGA AND PHYSICAL HEALING

After reading some of the miraculous claims appearing online, one may come away with the impression that iboga is a cure for everything from fungal and bacterial infections to acne, herpes, AIDs, and almost every imaginable illness. For the most part, the only evidence to support these claims consists of word of mouth, youtube videos, and written testimonies. This is not to say that all of these claims are false. In addition to being identified as a remedy for psychological and spiritual woes, West Africans have long-lauded iboga as a cure for a wide range of physical ailments.

When so many patients and providers repeat the same claims, it would be hasty to dismiss them. Nevertheless, the significant number of claims regarding iboga's physical healing properties is sharply contrasted by the lack of supporting clinical data. Definitive conclusions concerning iboga's true physical healing potential will require ongoing research. For individuals considering exploring iboga's potential to treat physical ailments, the best advice may be to connect directly with the source and track down an individual whose testimony appears online.

The following is a list of ailments and diseases for which iboga has been mentioned as a potential cure. The information here is presented only to cast light on the current state of affairs. It should in no way be mistaken as an attempt to promote or encourage iboga treatment as a remedy or cure.

Hepatitis C

Hepatitis C is an infectious liver disease most commonly transmitted through the blood and often linked to intravenous drug use. Some have claimed that ibogaine cures hepatitis C. This is unproven. However, there is more than enough anecdotal evidence to warrant further research.

In 2005, Howard Lotsof filed a patent application based upon his discovery that ibogaine alkaloids helped reduce hepatitis C symptoms.[186] These findings came from four case studies, two of whom were intravenous drug users treated during ibogaine therapy sessions.[187]

Since then, no further clinical studies have been undertaken. Again, the majority of evidence regarding ibogaine's ability to combat hepatitis C remains anecdotal. However, this is a case where an absence of evidence does not necessarily mean evidence of absence, particularly when so many people have made the same claim.

Parkinson's Disease

Parkinson's disease is a neuronal, age-related disorder that adversely affects the central nervous system. It results from the loss of brain cells called "dopaminergic neurons" (the brain's primary source of dopamine). Symptoms include loss of motor control, anxiety, depression, and eventually dementia.[188, 189]

Although certain treatments have shown results in slowing the onset of the disease, Parkinson's disease is presently incurable.[190]

Although its actions remain a mystery, ibogaine, along with its metabolite noribogaine has been shown to increase the production of glial cell line-derived neurotrophic factor (GDNF).[191] This hormone has been shown to promote the recovery and growth of these dopaminergic neurons resulting in symptomatic improvements in people with Parkinson's.

In ibogaine trials on Parkinson's afflicted rats, a 39% improvement in the off-medication motor sub-score of the Unified Parkinson's Disease Rating Scale (UPDRS) was recorded, along with a 61% daily living sub-score. A year later, zero side effects had been observed.[192] Additionally, some researchers have proposed ibogaines production of GDNF may play a role in repairing the same neurological pathways that have suffered damage from substance addiction.

Preliminary results, along with anecdotal evidence, points to the possibility that ibogaine may offer hope in the future. However, lack of research into its potential in treating Parkinson's still leaves a question mark over ibogaine's true efficacy.

Multiple Sclerosis

Multiple sclerosis is an autoimmune disease of the nervous system caused by exposure of the nerve cells in the brain and spinal cord.[193] Physical therapy may improve a patient's life quality, but a cure for MS is yet to be found.[194] MS medications have proven only moderately effective and can induce a range of adverse side effects. This has prompted more and more sufferers to seek alternative therapies, including ibogaine treatment.

What little clinical data exists regarding ibogaine and MS is purely theoretical.[195] However, there exists anecdotal reports from individuals claiming ibogaine helped with and in some cases caused a complete remission of their symptoms.

Fibromyalgia

Fibromyalgia is a medical condition that causes sufferers to experience extreme pain in various parts of the body.[196] Fibromyalgia is commonly linked to mood disorders, PTSD, anxiety, and depression.

Evidence of ibogaine's efficacy to help fibromyalgia sufferers is, to the author's knowledge, purely anecdotal.

19

IBOGAINE RELATED
FATALITIES

Any internet search for ibogaine treatment will likely bring up a slew of articles focusing on ibogaine-related deaths. Although extremely rare, deaths have indeed occurred. But not in the numbers that these sensationalist reports would indicate.

Research from animal studies indicates that ibogaine's LD50 (laboratory speak for 'lethal dose,') is around 327 mg/kg.[197] In layman's terms, this means ibogaine's toxicity is very weak. Although it's a gray area, clinical evidence strongly suggests that problems occur due to pre-existing heart conditions, the onset of withdrawals from substances ibogaine cannot fend off, and chiefly; the lingering presence of opioids in the bloodstream, which are thought to be amplified when the two compounds meet.

Mixing ibogaine with opioids is the chemical equivalent of injecting nitrous oxide into a speeding race car with a wobbly wheel. Although fatalities may not be directly attributable to ibogaine per se, its effects may have been the straw that broke the camel's back. This underscores one of the most (if not the most) crucial aspects of a medical ibogaine treatment: Do your homework, and undergo the relevant medical checks.

Ibogaine-related fatalities are undeniably tragic. However, the silver lining may be the emergence of a group of dedicated, conscientious ibogaine providers for whom patient screening and subsequent safety measures became a leading priority.

Some may find it disrespectful to attach the "martyr" label to the few individuals who passed away during an ibogaine treatment. However, this swing from underground, medically uninformed providers to trained, emergency-ready medical professionals grew from an ardent desire to avoid a repeat of such events.

The lack of experimental data into the biochemical sequence of events that trigger medical emergencies makes definitive conclusions difficult to draw. Although hard statistics on the topic are limited, one study revealed some interesting data.

In 2012, Dr. Kenneth Alper investigated all known cases of ibogaine-related fatalities that occurred outside of Gabon between 1990 and 2008. The research examined nineteen cases from around the world. Fifteen cases involved subjects seeking addiction treatment, a portion of whom were also addicted to cocaine and alcohol. In each case, no conclusive evidence was found to suggest ibogaine was the sole cause of death. Each incident included additional factors.[198]

One of the leading culprits was heart failure, thought to stem from ibogaine's capacity to prolong the QT interval, which is the time it takes for the ventricles to depolarize and repolarize between heartbeats.

Cardiac arrhythmias, resulting in seizures, were also experienced by individuals undergoing benzodiazepine or alcohol withdrawal.

If the chance of dying, no matter how remote, scares you, then the answer is simple. Find a reputable, medically trained provider, be thoroughly candid with them, and take the medical tests necessary to ensure your body is up to the challenge. Also, unless it's the night before and you've spoken with your provider, remember that one last hit for old times sake, either directly before or, God forbid, during treatment, is a terrible idea.

IF IT BLEEDS, IT LEADS

As ibogaine's profile rises, instead of reporting on its potential as a curative miracle, mainstream media outlets continue to focus on isolated incidents in which patients have died during treatment. "Dying to get clean," "Drug Cure Ends in Death," and "Illegal Killer Drug" are just a small selection of the sensationalist headlines that have appeared in recent media.[199, 200, 201] Whether they stem from lazy journalistic hackery, indifference, establishment interference, or a simple desire to boost tabloid sales, the result is the same; a skewed public perception of a "deadly" and "mysterious" root from the dark depths of the African jungle.

How ironic that the very demographic such headlines may dissuade are often those addicted to state-sanctioned substances far more dangerous, damaging, and culpable in countless more fatalities than ibogaine.

Nothing in what you have just read should be taken as an attempt to downplay the genuine perils that a small minority of at-risk individuals may be exposed to. While these risks certainly exist, they can be offset by research, planning, and medical testing. For the majority of otherwise healthy addicts, these risks are eclipsed by ibogaine's benefits.

20

IBOGA/IBOGAINE'S
PHYSICAL EFFECTS

Anyone thinking the iboga journey involves a pleasant body buzz might be in for a surprise. In some instances, notably among those seeking healing from addiction, it can be a rough physical ordeal, a trial by fire designed to reset and recalibrate one's physical vehicle via the quickest, most efficient means possible. In order to carry out its work, iboga may keep one glued to the ground, anesthetized, and barely able to move. Many (but not all) find this ride through the physiological washing machine an experience they are in no rush to repeat. Through this lens, ibogaine's classification in the US as a Schedule One substance - with a "high potential for abuse" reveals the plant's legal status for what it really is; a comic tragedy that exposes the gaping chasm between establishment doctrine and practical reality.

Now the good news. Despite the possibility of unpleasant physical sensations, most side effects are transient and tend to dissipate as one travels deeper into the journey. Furthermore, despite an awareness that their bodies are being vigorously scrubbed, many report their minds are entirely tuned to a different frequency. It's as if the physical discomfort occurs in a realm that occupies only a distant part of their attention, a place from which they feel far removed. Despite an awareness of being physically pounded, this out-of-body sensation may enable them to oversee their torture objectively, and even with detached curiosity. Considering at this point, they may be deep into some spectacularly strange mental terrain, such claims don't sound so far-fetched.

Some have likened it to opposing voices in their mind. One is saying, *"Hey, maybe you should focus on the fact you can't lift your head."* The other is saying *"or, you can focus on this once-in-a-life-time journey in search of your existential purpose."* Consequently, the fact you can't move your head may seem much less urgent.

If this makes the idea of experiencing ibogaine a little more reassuring, then great. However, to trivialize or downplay the potential seriousness of the side effects would be wrong. If protocols are followed, then the side-effects should present no danger whatsoever. However, forewarned is forearmed.

The following effects may depend on one's chosen iboga preparation. For instance, root bark may be more likely to cause nausea than total alkaloid extract or ibogaine HCL - the preferred preparation for addiction treatment. Regardless of the alkaloid makeup, or whether one's purpose is spiritual inquiry, mental health, or addiction treatment, these symptoms often overlap. While there may be some solid indicators, there is no hard and fast rule about when and where such side-effects will emerge.

Iboga(ine)s most commonly reported side effects include:

Ataxia
Ataxia is a dysfunction of the parts of the brain, namely the cerebellum, responsible for coordinating movement. In layman's terms, the body's GPS has gone haywire, and its fuel pump is

out of commission. Consequently, moving around unaccompanied can be a difficult, even dangerous prospect. Its capacity to hobble physical movement is a leading argument against iboga(ine) self-administration.

Nausea

As the ibogaine begins to flood the system, its opening task is to clean house. Like ayahuasca, ibogaine's purgative and cleansing effects may constitute an essential element of the experience and act to tune the body for the upcoming spiritual journey. Nevertheless, vomiting can still be dangerous. In the unlikely event things turn ugly, providers should be familiar with airway clearing procedures. At the very least, a sick bucket should be within easy reach.

Dehydration

Water should be on hand during the journey. Many say that consuming electrolyte-heavy liquids such as coconut water can be beneficial in the period leading up to the journey.

Cardiac irregularities

Iboga(ine) is known to cause bradycardia (slow heart rate) and a prolonged QT interval (the period between electrical heart waves). As mentioned, cardiac abnormalities are a chief suspect in several ibogaine-related fatalities. Patients on QT interval prolonging medications must inform their provider beforehand. For addiction treatments, an electrocardiogram test (ECG) is required to identify subjects with pre-existing QT interval irregularities. Some, but not all, providers offer these procedures.[202]

Tremors

Occasionally, patients experience involuntary bodily movements such as twitching, convulsions, and rhythmic muscle contractions. Although they may seem alarming there is little cause for concern.

Photosensitivity

Increased sensitivity to light can be offset by the provision of a comfortable eye mask and a provider who understands the benefits of conducting treatments during the night.

21

THE SUCCESS RATE
OF IBOGAINE

Questions surrounding ibogaine's true addiction beating potential are easier asked than answered. The first hurdle is defining how to measure "success."

If success is measured by ibogaine's capacity to dramatically alleviate one's burning desire to shoot up smack or celebrate with a liquid lunch, then the answer is very probably *"Yes."*[203]

If success is measured by ibogaine's capacity to help an addict understand and thus begin to confront the issues underlying their addictive behavior, then the answer is *"Highly likely."*

If the question is *"will ibogaine entirely eradicate the chances of relapse,"* or *"will it give me complete control over situations that previously triggered an immediate reach for the syringe or shot glass,"* then the short answer is *"no."* Or, at least, not on its own.

Ibogaine is the only compound on the planet known to induce such specific addiction-suppressing physical and neurological actions. However, the simple fact is that addiction can affect anyone regardless of age, character, professional status, gender, and more. It is often these social factors, along with the quality of aftercare and available resources, which determine ibogaine's true efficacy in combating addiction.

Given that many who provide ibogaine treatment do so anonymously, reliable data surrounding relapse rates versus long-term success rates remains sketchy. However, there have still been some admirable, professionally conducted attempts to assess the outcome of treatments.

Between 2012-2015, a team of researchers and treatment specialists performed a study to quantify long-term success rates for ibogaine-assisted opiate detoxification. Out of the 88 patients who received ibogaine treatment in a Mexican facility, 72% had been opioid-dependent for at least four years. 69% reported using opioids on a daily basis.[204]

The findings were as follows:

- 80% of patients reported ibogaine either stamped out or significantly lessened withdrawal symptoms.
- 50% of patients reported a reduced craving for opioids that lasted at least one week.
- 25% of patients reported a reduced craving for opioids that lasted three months or more.
- 30% of patients reported they had not used opioids again following ibogaine treatment. When interviewed a year after treatment, 54% of this sample had been clean for at least 12 months. 31% of this 54% had been clean for at least two years. It's important to note that 46% of the 30% who never used again following treatment were interviewed at various intervals of less than one year.
- 41% of patients reported ibogaine helped them remain opioid-free for six months.
- 70% of patients reported a relapse into opioid abuse.
- 48% reported a decrease from pretreatment levels of use. 11% of these patients eventually reached a state of opioid abstinence.

- 17% of patients reported their post-treatment levels of opioid consumption had not changed.

- 6% of patients reported their post-treatment levels of opioid consumption had increased.

- 61% of patients described ibogaine treatment as "very effective."

- 85% of patients reported that, in retrospect, their decision to undergo ibogaine treatment was a good one.

- 71% of patients reported ibogaine treatment to be "much better" than alternative treatments.

- 43% of patients reported a post-treatment upswing in both mood and psychological well-being that lasted a month or longer.

- 10% percent of patients reported this increase in psychological well-being lasted for longer than five months.[205]

This study shines a light on the gray areas surrounding ibogaine's success rates and once again forces us to ask what "success" means? To those searching for the "magic bullet," such results may sound disappointing. To those whom ibogaine acted as the key to an addiction-free life, the results were anything but.

These results also highlight that some addicts who fall victim to relapse may still acquire significant benefits from ibogaine. They show that in some cases, ibogaine treatment represented the first and most important step onto a path that led to reduced consumption, and in some cases, complete eventual abstention from opioids.

Essentially, these results again emphasize that ibogaine is an "addiction interrupter" and not a cure. It is a powerful tool that offers the addict pause to regroup, reflect, and capitalize on their gains. Nevertheless, it is still a tool. And like all tools, the outcome depends on the actions of whoever wields it.

The simple fact is that ibogaine is more successful in some cases than in others. In essence, it is the equivalent of a successful parole hearing. Freedom from the prison of addiction awaits, subject to conditions. Today, there are thousands who abided by those conditions enjoying levels of freedom and functionality they could once only have dreamed of.

22

IBOGA/IBOGAINE CONTRAINDICATIONS

Authors note: Much of the factual data presented herein was taken from the *Clinical Guidelines for Ibogaine-Assisted Detoxification*. This seminal work has saved lives, furthered ibogaine treatment's acceptance into the mainstream, and become an invaluable source of information for ibogaine providers. It was produced by members and associates of The Global Ibogaine Therapy Alliance. (GITA) Authors include Jonathan Dickinson, Jamie Mcalpin R.N. Clare Wilkins, Christine Fitzsimmons, Paige Guion R.N. Tanea Paterson, Douglas Greene. Bruno Rasmussen M.D. Edited by Jeffrey Kamlet M.D, DABAM, FASAM, and Roman Paskulin M.D. Ph.D.

The following information contains a list of substances that may interfere with, and in some cases, pose a real danger to those considering an ibogaine treatment.

Opioids

Opioids are substances derived from the alkaloids of the opium poppy that bind to the opioid receptors to provide somatic, pain-relieving effects. If used responsibly, they can be a powerful ally against physical pain. They also trigger euphoria and detachment, making them a target for addicts and recreational users.

Prolonged use results in tolerance, dependence, and guaranteed withdrawal symptoms for anyone who chooses to quit. Opioids include heroin, morphine, hydrocodone, oxycodone, and fentanyl. Together, these substances constitute the leading offenders in the opioid crisis. Regardless of their various legal status, they are cheap, highly addictive, and readily available. Their increased use, both in the US and globally, is rampant.

Opioids also include methadone and buprenorphine, which are the most common prescription option for those seeking to kick opioid dependence.

Methadone is more addictive than heroin, and its withdrawal symptoms are notoriously brutal. However, many have credited the mental clarity it affords as a significant aid in overcoming addiction, or at least delivering them to a place where they could begin to formulate an escape plan. If one's only alternative is street heroin, methadone is unquestionably the safer choice. Nevertheless, although the lesser of two evils, methadone is still a side-effect-ridden maintenance drug that fosters dependency.

Ibogaine has the power to help beat addiction to heroin and every opioid medication mentioned thus far. However, in the context of ibogaine treatment, the difference between the short-acting opioids (which are more rapidly expelled from the bloodstream) and long-acting methadone and buprenorphine becomes a potentially life or death variable.

Around two decades ago, observant ibogaine providers noticed that the relapse rate of methadone addicts eclipsed that of other opiates. The answer lay in the time period that different opioids remained in one's system. Unlike heroin, methadone and buprenorphine endure in the bloodstream for a longer period than ibogaine, eventually surpassing ibogaine's staying power to suppress post-treatment cravings.

It is uniformly agreed that the way to minimize risk is by trading long-acting opioids for short-acting opioids prior to treatment. Legal restrictions may make short-acting opioids more difficult to obtain. However, the temptation to use this as an excuse to return to cheaply available heroin should be strongly avoided.

The safe, successful use of ibogaine as an opioid addiction-interrupter carries with it a range of delicate medical and physiological variables. Answers surrounding the calculation of half-lives, timing, dosing, administration, and more have been won in the wake of trial, error, and studious observation by members of the ibogaine community. This includes scientists, medical professionals, providers, and multi-disciplinary participants, united in their commitment to the safe administration of ibogaine. The resulting knowledge base and subsequent protocols are, for the large part, outside the scope of this book. Anyone interested (and if you're planning treatment, then you should be) can find this material online.[206]

Alcohol

If consumed in relatively small quantities, alcohol kick starts the neurotransmitters that make one calm, relaxed, and happy. Consistent heavy drinking does the opposite and suppresses the activity in the exact same neurotransmitters. Eventually, more alcohol is needed to reproduce the desired effects. This condition is named alcohol tolerance and is a significant step on the short road towards alcohol dependence, or alcoholism.

If and when alcoholics decide to quit, these long-suppressed neurotransmitters bounce back with a vengeance. The brain becomes hyper excited, and somewhere between 1-4 days after one's last drink, the brutal, white-knuckle roller coaster ride of alcohol withdrawal begins. The severity of symptoms depends on how much and for how long one has been drinking. Ensuing tortures may include irritability, extreme anxiety, nausea, insomnia, and more. Although the aforementioned symptoms can be intensely uncomfortable, they generally do not pose a physical danger in and of themselves.

However, these symptoms are neurological. On a physical level, alcohol abuse may result in significant damage to one's body. Consequently, three other far more problematic alcohol-related factors; cardiomyopathy (heart problems), delirium tremens (DTs), and seizures, can occur.[207] Ibogaine has no power to alleviate or mitigate these withdrawal symptoms.

Research strongly suggests that ibogaine seekers who run the risk of alcohol withdrawal need to undergo complete detoxification for 5-7 days prior to treatment. During this period, withdrawal symptoms may appear without warning and with varying degrees of severity. Supervision of these overlapping and often complex symptoms may require professional medical supervision. As such, it is highly recommended (and by responsible providers, it's insisted) that the detox period is undergone in a medical setting where professional help is on hand.

For those just learning that ibogaine's ability to alleviate withdrawal symptoms does not apply to alcohol, this may come as bad news. Additionally, neither will a post-treatment patient wake up in a world of sweeping prohibitions, in which bars and liquor stores are no more. Like opioids, ongoing sobriety requires discipline and personal responsibility. The good news is that an ibogaine treatment can help with the psychological strength necessary to avoid relapse and yield enormous benefits for those looking to beat their booze dependence.

Following treatment, the noribogaine that remains in one's system can act as an ally against depression and the urge to reach for the bottle.[208] Many report that ibogaine can guide them through an introspective journey similar to that reported by opioid users. The visions and lessons imparted therein can help them process traumas, past events, underlying causes, and contributing factors.

Many recall their ibogaine treatment in terms of communion with a "higher power." Whether this is the same higher power which Alcoholics Anonymous believe to be an essential component of its 12-step program is another conversation.

As a rule, abstention from alcohol before an iboga(ine) session applies to everyone. For those dependent on alcohol, this advice is more than a mere suggestion. It is a crucial aspect of any safe, effective treatment.

Stimulants

The average bag of street cocaine can contain anything from talc, flour, washing powder, amphetamines, traces of diesel fuel, and various other chemical padding. However, it's the crystalline alkaloid named benzoylmethylecgonine that's responsible for cocaine's powerful stimulant effects. Throw in some baking soda, water, a heat source, and an urge for a cheaper, more potent, quicker acting high, and "voila"; now you have freebase cocaine or crack. Last but not least, there's methamphetamine, a powerful mood enhancer that promises temporary euphoria and sexual stamina for the price of ferocious comedowns and barbaric physical and psychological side-effects.

Although casual use of these substances, particularly cocaine, is common, the addictive pull of these drugs remains ultra-powerful for many. Their effect on the brain's dopaminergic reward pathways is explosive and immediate. In a short time, these pathways begin to get comfortable with the levels of dopamine release these stimulants induce. More drugs are needed to reach the same dizzyingly pleasurable heights that were first experienced. Like alcohol and heroin, this desensitization, or tolerance, is the first step towards addiction. In addition to temporarily feeling on top of the world, users can also expect paranoia, intestinal and digestive issues, loss of appetite, organ failure, heart problems, and possible strokes.

The physical and psychological addiction to these drugs (particularly crack and meth) can be challenging to beat, even with ibogaine treatment. Unlike opioids, where a single round of ibogaine can reset the opioid receptors to a pre-addicted state, neuroadaptations resulting from long-term crack, meth, and cocaine use are not so easily reversed. Ibogaine may alleviate cravings to some degree. However, the only thing that can restore natural serotonin levels and return the brain to its previous condition is time.

This is not to say ibogaine treatment holds no benefit for stimulant addicts—quite the opposite. Although concrete data is thin, anecdotal reports from patients and providers indicate ibogaine to be an effective aid in overcoming cravings. Although cravings will likely continue after ibogaine treatment, many subjects report them significantly decreased. Furthermore, some users have reported that cravings cease altogether a few days after treatment instead of weeks or even months without the ibogaine intervention.

Experiments on rats have concluded that smaller doses of ibogaine administered over a longer period of time can be effective in helping to overcome addiction to cocaine.[209] During the time it takes for the brain to recalibrate, smaller doses of ibogaine on a day-to-day basis may be more beneficial than the single flood dose used in opioid treatment.

That's the good news. Nevertheless, cocaine, meth, or crack addicts seeking ibogaine treatment must accept that post-treatment cravings may persist. Additionally, ibogaine's tendency to potentiate and amplify stimulants' effects means one's bloodstream must be stimulant-free prior to treatment. Like alcohol, withdrawal prior to treatment is essential. It is recommended that patients cease using crack and cocaine for at least seven days and methamphetamine five days prior to the administration of ibogaine.[210] This can be done alone. However, professional medical supervision makes for a safer, more comfortable ride.

Lastly, methylphenidate (Ritalin), dextroamphetamine (Adderall), and even caffeine are still stimulants. To be on the safe side, consumption of these substances should cease at least five days prior to treatment.[211]

Antidepressants

It would be inaccurate and irresponsible to state that pharmaceutical antidepressants have zero benefits whatsoever. In cases of severe depression where the patient requires immediate mood regulation, these medicines can be lifesaving. However, they also contain a high potential for addiction.

Unfortunately, in cases where traditional therapy fails, many healthcare professionals are left with no option but to prescribe long-term antidepressant regimens, knowing this may be the neurological equivalent of applying a band-aid to a bullet wound. In fairness, if this remains the only way to shield a patient from a disastrous downward spiral, then the provision of such remedies, no matter the consequences, may be entirely justified. Nevertheless, the side effects, which range from mild nausea to suicidal tendencies, have caused increasing numbers of medical professionals to refute their long-term efficacy.

Given the current state of human affairs, the true causes of depression are multi-layered and bewilderingly complex. In response to skyrocketing numbers of mental health problems, the marketplace now offers a smorgasbord of different antidepressants engineered to combat anxiety, OCD, PTSD, and more.

The complex neuro-mechanisms and chemicals that influence depression often depend on the individual. This can make correctly prescribing suitable medicine a challenging process of trial and error for medical professionals. Withdrawal symptoms may include nausea, headaches, insomnia, chills, physical aches and pains, and electric shock-like sensations. The long half-life of antidepressants means that these symptoms may last extended periods. Abruptly quitting or tapering down these medicines too rapidly can be complex, dangerous, and will likely cause significant discomfort.[212]

For the most part, antidepressant compounds all fall under the SSRI, SNRI, or MAOI class of medications.

SSRI / SNRIs

SSRI or SNRI stands for Selective Serotonin/Noradrenaline Reuptake Inhibitor. These medicines regulate serotonin's natural flow, effectively causing a serotonin bottleneck, resulting in mood elevation and other antidepressant properties.

Ibogaine also affects serotonin levels. This means an interaction between the two can lead to "serotonin syndrome." Although the effects are usually mild, this is not always the case. Those seeking ibogaine treatment must first undergo withdrawal from these medications. Ideally, this should be done under the supervision of a doctor or psychiatrist.[213]

MAOI Medications

Although Monoamine oxidase inhibitors (MAOIs) are still used, their potentially dangerous effects mean physicians and psychiatrists are reluctant to prescribe them, doing so only when SSRIs or SNRIs aren't up to the task. They work by preventing serotonin's metabolization, thus blocking the brain's natural serotonin distribution mechanisms. It's known that MAOIs amplify the effects of other psychoactive substances, including hallucinogens. Although its interactions with ibogaine are not yet understood, the chances that the two shouldn't be in bed together are thought to be high. Therefore, it's strongly recommended MAOI medications should be stopped at least a week to ten days before commencing ibogaine treatment.[214]

Benzodiazepines

Benzodiazepines or "benzos" is the umbrella name for a class of short, medium, or long-acting psychoactive sedatives that can help treat alcohol withdrawal, insomnia, anxiety, seizures, spasms, and more.

In fairness, since their market release in the 1960s, benzos have assisted the lives of many millions of people. Conversely, long-term use may cause depression, anxiety, amnesia, and in extreme cases, suicide. Despite the risks, benzos remain one of the most widely used and abused prescription drugs available. Their pleasant calming effects have resulted in the emergence of a lucrative and illicit benzo black market catering to recreational users. If used for long periods, tolerance to these medicines builds, resulting in unavoidable withdrawal symptoms for those seeking to kick them.

The risk of benzo dependency stems not from physical cravings but withdrawal symptoms. Like alcohol withdrawal, these symptoms fall into two categories. The first includes irritability, cognitive impairment, sleep disturbance, anxiety, pain, stiffness, sweating, headaches, nausea, and more. The second category includes potentially lethal seizures, usually suffered by high-dose or long-term users who enter withdrawal.

Ibogaine has no power to mitigate or offset any of benzodiazepine's withdrawal symptoms. Like alcohol, benzodiazepine problems have occurred not due to ibogaine per se but the onset of seizures after quitting benzos before or during the ibogaine treatment process. Consequently, safe treatment of those on a benzodiazepine regime requires clear, honest, and open dialogue between the patient and provider during the screening process.

Benzodiazepines affect an area of the brain that ibogaine simply does not.[215] Unfortunately, this was learned the hard way, in the wake of benzodiazepine-related fatalities that occurred during ibogaine treatments.[216]

Thankfully, benzo dependence does not necessarily disqualify someone from ibogaine treatment. Unlike other substances, benzodiazepines potency is not amplified by an ibogaine interaction. However, safe treatment requires adhering to specific protocols. When treating benzo users, the commonly accepted wisdom is that there is no middle ground. They either remain on benzos during treatment or quit them long before treatment.

Staying on Benzos

To offset the chance of fluctuating anxiety levels, patients taking short-acting benzodiazepines should switch to longer-acting medicines, namely diazepam or clonazepam, prior to treatment.[217] The only known negative consequence of benzodiazepine continuation during ibogaine treatment is that the psychoactive effects may lack their usual power and clarity.[218] Although a potential obstacle to the therapeutic process, this effect is not thought to be dangerous.

Coming off Benzos

The only safe way to wean oneself off benzodiazepine dependence is to gradually diminish their intake over an extended time period.[219] This tapering process can be tricky, may require many months and must be monitored by a physician. If rushed, the result may be the onset of benzo withdrawal's heaviest symptoms, including seizures. If one still seeks ibogaine treatment after the withdrawal process is complete, they must be careful to ensure that zero traces of benzodiazepine remain in their body beforehand.

Following medical confirmation that the body is benzo-free, people report ibogaine acts as a welcome closing chapter in waving their dependence goodbye. Furthermore, many report that a single dose of ibogaine effectively plugged the existential void that turned them to benzodiazepine in the first place.

Corticosteroids

Corticosteroids are a class of hormonal drugs very similar to the cortisol produced in the adrenal gland. Their medical use covers an extensive range of conditions, from brain tumors and multiple sclerosis to respiratory ailments, autoimmune diseases, and much more. Crucially, these compounds are known to affect the heart's QT interval, thereby making them a potential hazard for anyone seeking ibogaine treatment.[220]

Corticosteroids come in many different shapes and sizes, with varying half-lives. Prior to ibogaine treatment, it is highly recommended that anyone with a recent history of corticosteroid use consults a physician regarding how long these substances remain in their bloodstream. Only once they are eliminated should ibogaine treatment be considered safe.

Anabolic Steroids

The list of adverse effects stemming from the use of these compounds is long and varied. For potential ibogaine patients, there are two that stand out: liver damage and arrhythmia. An impaired liver may have trouble metabolizing ibogaine, and a stressed heart may be prone to arrhythmia.[221] For this reason, responsible ibogaine providers require certified documentation that a liver test and electrocardiogram have been undertaken prior to treatment.

Patients using testosterone replacements via shots, creams or gels, are advised to skip these on the day of their treatment.[222]

Thyroid Medications

Thyroid issues can lead to heart problems.[223] The most effective way to address these is through the prescription use of thyroid medications. These medications present no danger. The use of these medicines should be continued throughout the process to minimize the chance of any problems emerging during ibogaine treatment.[224]

Blood pressure medications

Beta-blockers may cause heart-related contraindications during an ibogaine treatment. It is advised their use be gradually tapered down over seven to fourteen days before treatment.[225]

Psychiatric medications

All psychiatric medications should be tapered down and stopped prior to ibogaine treatment. This process should be undertaken in communication with one's medication provider. People prescribed monthly shots, other long-acting psychiatric medicines, or those who cannot go without their medications for a minimum of five days are not suitable candidates for an ibogaine treatment.[226]

23

IBOGAINE SYNTHETICS

In 1996, pharmacologists developed a synthetic derivative of ibogaine named 18-Methoxycoronaridine (18-MC).[227] Like ibogaine, 18-MC proved effective in interrupting symptoms of addiction in rodents.[228] It was developed under the premise that ibogaine, or something similar, would only ever gain mainstream acceptance once the psychoactive properties were excluded. Unlike ibogaine, which occurs naturally and is therefore non-patentable, 18-MC is man-made. This patentability, combined with its ability to skirt the psychoactive effects, established 18-MC as a potentially lucrative project for pharmaceutical companies.

In September 2012, Savant HWP was awarded a $6.5 million grant from the National Institute on Drug Abuse (NIDA) to help fund the preclinical development of 18-MC in treating cocaine abuse.[229] Eighteen months later, Savant HWP filed an application with the United States Food and Drug Administration (FDA) for 18-MC to be registered as an Investigational New Drug (IND). This would effectively grant permission for the company to begin conducting human trials. At this time of writing, the IND application remains under FDA review.[230]

In 2020, researchers at the University of California reported creating a nontoxic and non-hallucinogenic ibogaine synthetic shown to alleviate depression and addictive traits in rodents. At the time of writing, data surrounding 'tabernanthalog,' or TBG is scarce.[231]

While proponents argue that these lab-engineered synthetics represent the best current shot at a medically accepted looka-like, opponents argue that such products don't trigger iboga's complex psycho-spiritual actions. During iboga(ine) treatments, people report a visionary return to past traumas that laid the emotional groundwork for their addictions. Many claim that these visions play an indispensable role in overcoming the psychological aspect of addiction.

24

IBOGA(INE)'S LEGAL STATUS

The current debate over why iboga and its derivatives remain outlawed in so many places runs deep. The official line is that iboga remains illegal due to its powerful psychoactive effect. Despite volumes of evidence to support ibogaine's effectiveness in addiction recovery, in the United States, it remains a Schedule One drug in all but a handful of States and Counties. This means it has "no currently accepted medical use and a high potential for abuse." Many who have experienced treatment in either a clinical or ceremonial setting would argue both of these decrees to be as laughable as they are ludicrous.

The following information lists only the countries in which iboga has surfaced on the legal radar. Here, iboga's legal status varies from outright bans to welcome embrace. If a country goes unmentioned, it means that iboga has gone unnoticed or ignored by the law, making it 'unregulated' and neither legal nor illegal at the time of writing. In practical terms, this means these countries are free to do what they wish, including allowing ibogaine treatment centers to operate within their borders. At the time of writing, this information is correct. Obviously, the law is subject to change in both the following countries and any countries where iboga becomes a future topic.

Australia – Controlled

Ibogaine is a Schedule Four substance; a prescription-only medicine to be supplied only by a pharmacist or someone with the legal authority to do so. Although possession of ibogaine-containing plants is legal, the import and sale of any iboga products is strictly prohibited and carries heavy penalties.

Belgium – Illegal

In 1998 ibogaine and its related compounds were placed under the *Royal Decree on psychotropic substances.* Possession, supply, import, export, and cultivation of ibogaine is illegal without permission from the Minister of Public Health,

Brazil – Controlled

In January 2016, The President of the National Association of the Study of Drug Policy (CONED-SP) took action that placed Brazil on the front lines of global psychedelic research. A declaration was issued calling for extensive scientific research into a range of psychoactive substances. The government permitted the administration of ibogaine to patients in a hospital environment with medical supervision and control.

Canada – Controlled

Canada listed ibogaine as a Natural Health Care Product in 2009, making it legal to import and possess. In the wake of ibogaine's deregulation, several treatment clinics have emerged across the country to treat severe substance addictions.

In 2015, Health Canada received reports of a serious adverse

reaction following the ingestion of a pharmaceutical-grade ibogaine product sold under the name Remogen. Although anecdotal evidence suggests the ibogaine may have been self-ad-
ministered, Health Canada declined to clarify where this report
originated. Health Canada seized all ibogaine-containing products from Phytostan Enterprise Inc, the Quebec-based dis-
tributor of Remogen, and asked them to stop selling the products.[232] Health Canada subsequently issued a statement saying
they were working with the Canada Border Services Agency to
prevent future importation of ibogaine products.[233] At the time
of writing, ibogaine treatment remains available in Canada.

Costa Rica – Legal
Ibogaine is legal in Costa Rica, making it a leading location for
those seeking treatment,

Denmark – Controlled
Ibogaine and its derivatives are listed as a euphoric substance
"used for medical and scientific purposes with substantial
controls."[234] Upon receipt of permission from The Ministry
of Health, ibogaine may be administered by medical professionals. Outside of this, ibogaine is illegal to possess, cultivate,
import, and distribute.

Finland – Illegal
In 2014 the Finnish narcotics act was amended to include ibogaine among a range of *"psychoactive substances banned from
the consumer market."* Following a period of evaluation, these
substances were decreed a *"danger to public health and safety."*

Since then, possession cultivation, import, and unauthorized distribution of ibogaine are punishable by up to one year in prison.

France – Illegal

In 2006 a French male with a history of drug abuse was found dead after self-administering root bark. The autopsy revealed the victim had taken methadone, valium, and showed symptoms consistent with a drug overdose. Despite this, the autopsy report, made no mention of the methadone or valium, and concluded the victim's death resulted from ibogaine uptake.[235] Tabernanthe Iboga and ibogaine were added to a list of controlled substances the following year. Ibogaine remains illegal to possess or distribute.

Gabon – Legal

Iboga's physical and spiritual home. Here, the Tabernanthe Iboga plant is both legal and celebrated.

Hungary – Illegal

Ibogaine is listed under the New Psychotropic Substances of Government Regulation on drugs and psychotropic substances.[236] Possession, cultivation, purchase, import, and export of ibogaine are subject to strict licensing.

Ireland – Uncertain

In 2010 the Irish Government passed the *Psychoactive Substances Act* in a bid to crackdown on legal highs. The purposely ambiguous law deliberately declines to name specific compounds and was drawn up as a generic response to the ever-changing chemical structure of substances available online and in head shops. It defines psychoactive substances as a;

> "product, preparation, plant, fungus or natural organism which has, when consumed by a person, the capacity to produce stimulation or depression of the central nervous system of the person, resulting in hallucinations or a significant disturbance in, or significant change to, motor function, thinking, behavior, perception, awareness or mood."[237]

Ibogaine clearly falls within the scope of this act. However, the wording goes on to state that the law does not apply to *"medicinal products,"* as defined and approved by the European Economic Community (EEC), of which Ireland is a member. Although the EEC has yet to approve ibogaine as a "medicinal product," *Directive 65/65 EEC* makes clear that even without this approval, psychoactive substances may be used by medical professionals of EEC member states. It also makes provision for the research and development of these "medicinal products," which may provide researchers with greater elbow room than in countries where ibogaine is banned outright.[238]

Israel – Illegal

In early 2015 the Israeli government placed ibogaine under *The Fight against the Phenomenon of the Use of Dangerous Substances Law.* Possession, supply, import, or cultivation are illegal and subject to penalties.

Italy – Illegal

As of 2016, ibogaine and the Tabernanthe Iboga plant were classified as Schedule One drugs due to their hallucinogenic properties and effects on the central nervous system. Possession or distribution carries penalties, including jail time.

Mexico – Legal

Ibogaine's unregulated status, along with its proximity to the US, makes Mexico the leading location for those seeking ibogaine treatment. Consequently, a good number of treatment centers have emerged there in the past decade.

New Zealand – Legal

Noting the failed attempts of other countries to ban psychoactive substances and the rapid marketplace re-appearance of the same compounds with different name tags, the New Zealand government took a radically different and much more rational approach. In 2009, Medsafe (the medical regulatory body run by the New Zealand Ministry of Health) ruled that ibogaine's safety profile and low potential for misuse qualified it to be classified under the Medicines Act of 1981. Although the government controls supply, ibogaine is now available as a prescription medication and can be administered by licensed professionals.

Norway – Illegal

Possession, cultivation, distribution, and import are illegal and subject to penalties.[239]

Portugal

In 2001, Portugal decriminalized possession and use of all drugs, including iboga(ine).

South Africa – Controlled

Before 2016, ibogaine was freely available as a traditional medicine and used by several treatment centers. In May 2016, the South African Medical Control Council (MCC) classified ibogaine as a schedule 6 substance. They cited a lack of evidence concerning iboga(ine)'s safety or efficacy and the deaths that had occurred after ibogaine was used without medical supervision. Ibogaine production and supply now requires a permit from the Director-General. A licensed medical professional may conduct ibogaine treatment. Possession of ibogaine is legal only when accompanied by a prescription issued by an authorized prescriber.

Sweden – Illegal

In accordance with the government's stated aim of creating a "drug-free society," Sweden continues to enforce some of the strictest drug laws in Europe. Although data suggests that drug use in Sweden falls below the global average, many researchers argue that this is due to broader social and economic factors and has little to do with drug policy.[240, 241] Disregard for proven harm reduction measures among Swedish government policy-makers has led to serious consequences for intravenous drug users. These include a massive spike in drug-induced deaths and alarmingly high rates of hepatitis C contraction.[242] In 1985, ibogaine was classified as a Schedule One substance, implying it has no medical value. It is illegal to possess or distribute even for medical purposes.

Switzerland – Illegal

Possession, cultivation, distribution, and import are illegal and subject to penalties.[243]

United Kingdom – Legal to possess. Illegal to supply

In 2016, British policy-makers placed ibogaine within the wide-ranging Psychoactive Substances Act. This act was designed as a "silver bullet" to throw a net over the growing influx of legal highs entering the country. It defines a psychoactive substance as anything *"capable of producing a psychoactive effect in a person who consumes it."* Unsurprisingly, critics of the bill have deemed it too broad to be enforceable, let alone effective.

It is a criminal offense to export, import, produce or supply ibogaine. The law makes no mention of personal possession of ibogaine, thus making it technically legal. Subsequently, several treatment centers have emerged in the United Kingdom.

In early 2017, two British men were charged with manslaughter over the death of a heroin addict at their ibogaine facility. The pathologist concluded it unlikely that ibogaine was the cause of the man's death, and the pair were cleared of manslaughter. However, upon being convicted of fraud, failure to register as service providers, and supplying unauthorized medicinal products, the men were jailed for twenty-one months and nine months respectively.[244]

United States – Illegal (a few states and counties notwithstanding)

Ibogaine has been a Schedule One controlled substance since 1970. This means:

1. It has a high potential for abuse.
2. It has no currently accepted medical use in treatment in the United States.
3. There is a lack of accepted safety for the use of it under medical supervision.[245]

Despite evidence confirming these descriptions of ibogaine are at best inaccurate and at worst willfully ignorant, the US federal government has done little to re-examine ibogaine's legal status. Cultivation, import, possession, use, and distribution largely remain illegal and subject to penalties.

In 2015, state politicians from Vermont and New York put forward bills H741 and A08356 to combat the growing impact of the nationwide opioid crisis.[246, 247] Although the specifics of these bills vary slightly, they are united in their aim of making ibogaine legally available as an addiction treatment. In June 2019, Oakland became the first area to decriminalize the use of iboga. In 2020 Ann Arbor, Michigan, Santa Cruz, California, and Washington DC followed suit.

Uruguay – Legal to possess

Possession of drugs for personal use is legal in Uruguay. If arrested, it's up to the state to decide whether the quantity in possession amounts to more than personal use.

25

THE IBOGAINE
BILL OF RIGHTS

H oward Lotsof originally authored the Ibogaine Patients Bill of Rights for the Dora Weiner Foundation, a non-profit formed to promote the rights of addicts being treated for drug dependence. Although produced during the early days of the US ibogaine movement, it remains as relevant as ever.

The Ibogaine Patient's Bill of Rights

1. You have the right to understand and use these rights. If for any reason you do not understand your rights, or you need help in understanding your rights, the ibogaine provider must make assistance available, including an interpreter.
2. You have the right to be informed of the dose and form of ibogaine you will receive.
3. You have the right to receive complete information about your diagnosis, treatment, and prognosis.
4. You have the right to participate in all decisions about your treatment.

5.   You have the right to receive treatment without discrimination as to race, color, religion, sex, national origin, disability, or sexual orientation.

6.   You have the right to receive considerate and respectful care in a clean and safe environment free of unnecessary restraint.

7.   You have the right to be informed of the name, position, experience, and credentials of the primary caregiver who will be in charge of your ibogaine therapy.

8.   You have the right to receive all the information that you need to give informed consent for any proposed procedure or treatment you will receive and the possible risks and benefits of the proposed procedure or treatment.

9.   You have the right to refuse treatment and be told what effect this may have on your health.

10. You have the right to be informed of alternate therapies.

11. You have the right to privacy while undergoing ibogaine treatment and confidentiality of all information and records regarding your care.

12. You have the right to review your treatment record without charge and obtain a copy of your treatment record for which your provider can charge a reasonable fee, with the understanding that you can not be denied a copy solely because you cannot afford to pay.

13. You have the right to complain without fear of reprisals about the care and services you are receiving, and to have the provider respond to you.

14. You have the right to file a Grievance Report and have a patient advocate intervene on their behalf.

Ibogaine Patient's Responsibilities

By accepting the above-granted rights, you are also accepting the following responsibilities:

1. You are responsible for providing accurate and complete information about past illnesses, hospitalizations, medications, and other health-related matters.
2. You are responsible for informing their treatment providers and other caregivers if they anticipate problems in following prescribed treatment.
3. You must take responsibility for requesting additional information or clarification about their health status or treatment when they do not fully understand the current information or instructions.[248]

26

IN CASE OF RELAPSE

Cases in which ibogaine has been a one-shot miracle cure for addiction are the exception and not the rule. Whether it be a single moment of weakness, a lack of willpower, inadequate support, or any other factors that compel a return to old patterns, the unfortunate truth is that most of those who seek ibogaine treatment for addiction are prone to relapse.

Sadly, the traditional view of relapse into addiction sees it as a failure. This conclusion does little to support the addict or engender the self-esteem necessary to achieve full recovery. If a relapse occurs, while the answer may be more complex, the question is simple; is this obstacle an impregnable barrier or a mere pothole on the road to recovery? The answer should always be the latter.

For many, relapse is a part of the package. The key is to keep trying, keep fighting, and to prepare and expect for the day when the light at the end of the tunnel is finally reached. It is heartening to note that most who experience post-ibogaine relapse still report reduced drug consumption and improved quality of life. They say that although their treatment was not a one-shot cure, it nevertheless provided a considerable boost.

Although relapse is never what one hoped for, it is a well-worn path for many who eventually broke free from the chains of addiction. These people are the ones who decided to be defined not by their temporary backslide but their commitment to remain in recovery. Such individuals may advocate the importance of not being too hard on oneself, nor consider one's relapse a failure. Instead, to take pride in one's efforts and use them as a source of strength instead of weakness.

Although previously noted, the following piece of critical information cannot be overemphasized: If, after ibogaine treatment, one must return to using, even if just a single hit-for-old-times-sake, anything that comes close to the veteran doses of the past could cause a fatal overdose.

27

THE MODERN HISTORY OF IBOGA: A TIMELINE

Nowadays, due to a widening recognition of iboga's anti-addictive and spiritual properties, a whole new history of the plant is emerging. The following timeline highlights the major steps iboga has taken in its migration from the jungles of Africa to the laboratories, therapy centers, and ceremonial settings of the west.

1819: During passage through Gabon, British explorer Thomas Edward Bowditch pens the first known written reference to "Eroga" (iboga). He describes it as a *"favorite but violent medicine."*[249]

1864: French naval surgeon Griffin Du Bellay returns to his homeland with a specimen of iboga acquired in Gabon. He describes it as an inebriating tonic and aphrodisiac which causes sleeplessness.[250]

1885: Father Henri Neu writes a manuscript entitled *"Le Gabon."* It describes iboga as a powerful potion that provides access to hidden realms in which subjects experience visions of future events. According to Neu, he who drinks iboga *"falls into a deep sleep during which he is obsessed by uninterrupted dreams which, until the time that he awakens, he takes to be actual events."*[251]

1898: German colonists in Gabon note that Tabernanthe Iboga has an *"exciting effect on the nervous system so that its use is highly valued on long and tiring marches, on lengthy canoe voyages, and long night-watches."*[252]

1901: J. Landrin and E. Dybowsky isolate iboga's principal psychoactive alkaloid. They name it "Ibogaine."[253]

1901-1905: Researchers perform the first pharmacodynamic studies of iboga. Research focuses on iboga's fatigue-fighting properties. In 1905, iboga is recommended as a treatment for asthenia (an abnormal lack of physical energy) at a suggested intake of between 10 to 30 mg per day.[254]

1939-1970: Ibogaine is sold in France in 8mg tablets under the name *Lambarène*. It is marketed as a "neuromuscular stimulant," effective in combating fatigue and depression and promising a speedier recovery for sufferers of infectious diseases.[255] Lambarene's strength-giving properties are noted among endurance athletes and those engaged in strenuous activity. The International Olympic Committee would later recognize these properties and place ibogaine on the banned substances list.

1943: While researching the pharmaceutical potential of the ergot fungus, Albert Hofman, a Swiss scientist, unwittingly sired the most powerful lab-synthesized compound in neuropharmacological history: Lysergic acid diethylamide (LSD). After accidentally ingesting a chemical residue that had stuck to his hand, he slipped into a *"not unpleasant intoxicated like condition, characterized by an extremely stimulated imagination,"* and perceived an *"uninterrupted stream of fantastic pictures, extraordinary shapes, and an intense, kaleidoscopic play of colors."*

In the following decades, the popularity of LSD skyrocketed in the United States. Its widespread use would eventually set the stage for the prohibition of iboga.

1955: Harris Isbell, Director of Addiction Research for the National Institute of Mental Health and one of the chief psychedelic researchers in the CIA's MKUltra program, administers ibogaine to eight detoxified morphine addicts in doses of up to 300mg.[256]

During this period, the Central Intelligence Agency's investigations into psychedelics as a potential weapon against Communism extended to North American universities. Professors and students gained access to LSD, thus catalyzing the birth of the beatnik movement.

1956: The US Government grants Patent 2813873 after a complete organic synthesis of the ibogaine alkaloid is achieved in a laboratory.[257]

1956-57: Jurg Schneider, a pharmaceutical researcher, discovers ibogaine significantly increases the effects of morphine and other opiates.[258] This discovery would later be proposed as a causal factor in the deaths that occurred in later decades, particularly in cases when heroin addicts had taken a hit directly before an ibogaine treatment.

1957: W.I. Taylor publishes the first definitive description of ibogaine's chemical structure.[259]

1962-1963: During breakfast with a chemist friend, Howard Lotsof is presented with a small vial of an "African Hallucinogen that lasts 36 hours." Initially hesitant, he eventually ingests the ibogaine and experiences a prolonged ordeal that leaves him exhausted and intent on never taking the compound again. Soon thereafter, he took a walk outside to discover he was no longer in a state of narcotic withdrawal. He stated:

> "I looked at this large tree in front of me, and I looked at the clouds in the sky, and I realized for the first time in my life that I was not frightened."

Shortly after that, Lotsof administered 6–19 mg/kg of ibogaine to nineteen individuals, seven of whom were addicted to opiates. Ibogaine's effectiveness in treating withdrawal symptoms enters the record.[260]

1960-1970: The protest movements that emerged in the 1960s sprang from legitimate grievances against political power structures. Unfortunately, images of blissed-out, promiscuous, half-naked hippies appearing on TVs didn't help their cause. Spurred by reports of isolated criminal incidents within the movement, the media set out to paint a group of largely peaceful, anti-establishment protesters as an amoral, drug-addled gang of drop-outs. LSD was lampooned as the ringleader of a movement hellbent on the corrosion of middle-class American values. In the summer of 1966, the trigger was pulled on the psychedelic hit job that would cripple ibogaine research for decades.

1962-2010: Following his life-changing ibogaine experience, Howard Lotsof stated;

"the most important thing that I could perceive of doing with my life was to produce ibogaine as an available, medically approved drug." [261]

Over the next half-century, Lotsof would emerge as a major figure in the campaign to establish ibogaine in the west. His extensive research would pave the way for other researchers to begin serious scientific studies into ibogaine's potential. He went on to produce the "Ibogaine Patient's Bill of Rights." He also founded The Global Ibogaine Therapy Alliance (GITA), a not-for-profit organization devoted to supporting the sacramental and therapeutic use of iboga in a safe, responsible, and sustainable manner.

Howard Lotsof died in 2010. Shortly before his passing, he was presented with the Robert C. Randall Award for Achievement in the Field of Citizen Action.

1965: The total synthesis of ibogaine is achieved.[262]

1966: Despite positive evidence for the therapeutic use of certain psychedelics, the US Government enacts sweeping prohibitions banning their possession. This further sets the stage for ibogaine's subsequent prohibition.

1967-1970: The World Health assembly labels ibogaine a hallucinogen *"likely to cause dependency or endanger human health."* The US Food and Drug Administration classify ibogaine as a schedule one substance, placing it in the same group as the very substances it had been proven to help with. In France, Lamberene is withdrawn from the market.[263]

1969: Dr. Claudio Naranjo, a Chilean-born psychiatrist, is awarded a French patent for the psychotherapeutic administration of ibogaine.[264] Naranjo's work focused on the psychotherapeutic benefits of ibogaine for patients seeking closure for persistent emotional issues.[265] His findings praise ibogaine's ability to allow a patient to objectively revisit past experiences and resolve deeply ingrained personal conflicts. Dr. Naranjo would go on to become one of the most influential voices in the global ibogaine advocacy movement.

1970: While covering the Wisconsin primaries for Rolling Stone magazine, Journalist Hunter. S. Thompson accused Democratic Party candidate Edmund Muskie of being addicted to ibogaine. Although the piece was satire, many readers took this unfounded accusation seriously. Thompson's Rolling Stone piece was cited as a contributing factor in Muskie losing the nomination to George McGovern.

1970s – 1980s: The strongly enforced US ban on hallucinogens drives both the discussion and use of ibogaine underground. Meanwhile, the use of heroin and later crack begins its rapid and devastating infiltration of poor US communities. In wealthier circles, cocaine use skyrockets

Inspired by anti-drug initiatives taken to defend their communities by civilian groups such as the black panthers, other groups begin to organize campaigns denouncing governmental drug policy. Their slogans, *"Cures not Wars,"* and *"Treatment not Punishment,"* reflected their belief that drug use is a medical rather than a criminal issue.

1982 Denmark: In the self-proclaimed autonomous neighborhood of Christiana, severe heroin addicts receive treatment with a concentrated iboga preparation named "Indra extract."[266]

1985: Howard Lotsof is awarded US Patent 4857523 for the use of ibogaine to treat opiate-dependent individuals.[267] Further patents are granted over the next several years, allowing research into ibogaine's ability to treat alcohol, nicotine, cocaine, and polysubstance abuse.[268, 269, 270, 271]

1986: After a series of attempts to bring ibogaine to the attention of major drug companies prove fruitless, Howard Lotsof forms NDA International, a private pharmaceutical company. NDA International provided funding for research, resulting in over 60 peer-reviewed publications related to the structure and actions of ibogaine and its related compounds.

1987: Lotsof travels to Gabon with a cocaine-addicted friend, Bob Sisko. Lotsof appeals to Gabonese President Ali Bongo to make an exception to the embargo on the export of iboga on the grounds that the root is needed to demonstrate the plant's efficacy to the FDA. Bongo agrees and ships forty kilos of root bark to NDA International, declaring it to be a gift from Gabon to America and the world.

After experiencing ibogaine's effects first-hand, Bob Sisko would subsequently become an influential figure in the ibogaine movement.[272] Later in the year, Sisko and Lotsof manage to convince the Gabonese President to make a further shipment, which finds its way to the Pharmacology department of Erasmus University in Rotterdam. Four years later, these studies would produce the first paper showing that ibogaine effectively reduced opiate withdrawal symptoms in animals.[273]

1989: Howard Lotsof applies for a patent for the use of ibogaine to treat alcohol addiction. Later in the year, he contracts Dr. Stanley Glick, head of the Department of Pharmacology at

Albany College of Medicine, to begin rigorous scientific testing of ibogaine. The data acquired from animal tests supports ibogaine's capacity to reduce both withdrawal symptoms from opioids and the desire to self-administer opioids and cocaine.[274, 275]

1990 Holland: Bob Sisko acquires ibogaine and begins treatments in Holland. Patients include Nico Adriaans, founder of the Dutch "junkie bond" movement and head of The Dutch Addict Self Help Group (DASH). Following successful treatment for addiction to heroin, methadone, and tobacco, Adriaans proceeds to treat other addicts. By 1993, NDA International, DASH, and INTASH (The center for addiction research at Erasmus University) had collectively performed 45 treatments.[276] These results were medically evaluated and subsequently published by Dr. Ken Alper in the American Journal of Addictions.[277]

1991-92: Based on mounting evidence suggesting ibogaine's efficacy, NIDA (National Institute on Drug Abuse) conducts preclinical toxicology studies and begins to compile data on human protocols. The same year, Jan Baastians, a pioneering psychiatrist famed for his work with LSD on WW2 concentration camp victims, begins work alongside Howard Lotsof in treating heroin addicts with ibogaine.

1993: Dr. Deborah Mash, Professor of Neurology at the University of Miami, approaches the FDA Advisory Panel to consider an application to begin clinical trials. The application is granted, and research begins.

The same year, a 24-year-old female patient was pronounced dead 19 hours after ingesting ibogaine. Charred tin foil was found among the victims' possessions, suggesting that shortly before taking ibogaine she used heroin. These findings supported the idea that ibogaine, when ingested alongside opiates, significantly increases heroin's toxicity.

Although Dr. Mash's clinical trials continued for a period, funding disputes between the University of Miami and NIDA brought research to a close before it had produced the desired results. Shortly thereafter, NIDA suspended all further ibogaine-related research.

Mid-1990s-Present: In the face of growing political and corporate opposition, legal ibogaine treatment centers in North America and Europe find it increasingly difficult to operate. They begin scouting foreign locations in which to continue their work legally.

1992–1994: As the western demand for ibogaine rises, a series of cultural protection laws are passed that outlaw the export of iboga from Gabon.[278] Although these laws were established to protect the Tabernanthe Iboga plant from poaching and over-harvesting, reports suggest they also gave rise to an underground, black market export industry.

1993: Robert Goutarel, a French chemist, hypothesizes that the iboga journey shares similar characteristics with REM sleep. Goutarel suggests that the anti-addictive properties of ibogaine may result from its ability to induce a state of heightened neuroplasticity. This provides a window during which the patient's psychological links and motivations for using addictive substances are weakened.[279]

1994 Italy: A small, informal treatment network is established after an Italian chemist develops his own method of extracting ibogaine from the root bark. Between 35-40 people receive treatment.

1994 Panama: Howard Lotsof begins treating patients at a clinic in Panama.

1995 Slovenia: Marko Resinovic, founder of the Slovenian Iboga Foundation, reports the emergence of a loosely organized ibogaine scene, comprised principally of opioid addicts.[280]

1996: In response to mounting governmental pressure to end all ibogaine-related research, Dr. Deborah Mash relocates to the Caribbean island of St Kitts.[281] Although a few treatment centers are already operating, this is the first to insist patients undergo medical screening before treatment. Approximately seventy addicts undergo treatment here.[282]

1996 – Present: In 1996, researchers developed a synthetic derivative of ibogaine named 18-Methoxycoronaridine (18-MC).[283] Like ibogaine, 18-MC test results demonstrate the mitigation of opioid withdrawal symptoms and long-lasting decreases in cravings for cocaine, methamphetamine, morphine, nicotine, and alcohol.[284] 18-MC also demonstrated potential in the treatment of Parkinson's, obesity, and abnormal eating behavior.[285] Due to a lack of effect on serotonin levels, MC-18 does not trigger the visions and hallucinations that many ibogaine advocates and providers consider crucial to the psychological efficacy of treatments.[286]

In February 2014, Savant HWP registered an Investigational New Drug (IND) application with the FDA.[287]

1997: Dana Beal co-authors the book *The Ibogaine Story: Report on the Staten Island Project.*

In the late 1960s, Beal became a prominent member of a counter-cultural activist group known as the "Yippie" movement. In the decades that followed, Beal emerged as an outspoken critic of the drug war and a vocal proponent of the benefits of ibogaine's curative potential. His work continues to this day.

1998: United Kingdom: An ibogaine scene begins to develop in the United Kingdom in the wake of a lengthy ibogaine article published in the *London Times,* along with the publication of *The Ibogaine Story.*[288, 289]

1999 The Netherlands: Although Holland witnessed the emergence of ibogaine treatments in the late 1980s and early 1990s, anecdotal evidence suggests they decreased in subsequent years. In 1999, an independent provider began offering treatment from her home on the outskirts of Amsterdam. As of November 2000, she claimed to have treated more than 20 individuals, many of whom journeyed from the United States. The majority of treatments were administered for substance dependence, while a minority of patients underwent sessions for "psycho-spiritual development." She stated that proper aftercare, followed by non-drug-centered social networks for the patient to return to, were crucial in determining addiction treatments' success.

In the same year, thirty-three heroin addicts were given ibogaine as part of an NDA International study into heroin detoxification. The results showed that two days after ibogaine treatment, twenty-five subjects reported complete remission of their heroin addiction, with zero withdrawal symptoms or cravings.[290]

2000 Czech Republic: Approximately eighteen opiate-dependent addicts and sixty non-addicts begin receiving treatment. The treatment provider terminated operations within a year. The provider felt strongly that ibogaine treatment alone without structured aftercare offered limited benefits for addicts.

2000 South Africa: Dan Lieberman, a South African ethno-botanist and Bwiti initiate, passes away. Prior to his death, he arranged Bwiti initiations for Europeans and Americans in Gabon. He also arranged treatment for numerous heroin addicts in South Africa. As an ardent advocate of Bwiti culture Lieberman considered "set and setting" to be vital in gaining the most from the iboga experience. He believed components of the Bwiti initiation ceremony to be of enormous benefit in optimizing ibogaine's efficacy in addiction treatment.

2000: Gabonese President Omar Bongo declares iboga "a cultural heritage strategic reserve."

2001 – 2006: The use of ibogaine in addiction treatment reportedly increases four-fold.[291]

2002: Howard Lotsof collaborates with Boaz Wachtel to co-author *The Manual for Ibogaine Therapy*. This is one of the first publications to outline a comprehensive set of protocols for the safe administration of ibogaine.

2007 France: Following an ibogaine-related death, a nationwide ban is imposed on ibogaine and its related compounds.

2009 Mexico: Sayulita, Mexico, is chosen to host the first International Ibogaine Conference. The conference marked the first coming together of leading pioneers in the ibogaine field. Treatment providers and others joined ibogaine community heavyweights such as Howard Lotsof, Dr. Kenneth Alper, and Bruno Rasmussen MD to discuss topics including ibogaine mechanisms, case studies, the importance of aftercare, ethical sourcing of iboga, threats to Bwiti life-ways, and more. This

conference marked a crucial shift in how ibogaine was discussed and has become one of the community's most important gatherings. The conference has taken place on four further
occasions in Barcelona (2010), Vancouver (2012), Durban
(2014), and Tepoztlan (2016.)

2012: Yann Guignon, a French ibogaine advocate and Bwiti
member, submits a report to Gabonese President Ali Bongo
Ondimba. His findings are based on his own research, scientists' research, and the views of representatives from the different branches of Bwiti culture. The report cautions against
iboga's potentially imminent disappearance from the public
domain and the importance of taking steps to protect this
precious natural resource. Among other factors, he cites the
sharp increase in global demand for iboga root bark and its
extracts.

President Ondimba takes note and bans the export of iboga
by integrating it into the Nagoya protocol, an international
treaty designed to protect the "genetic resources" of each of
the 93 signatory nations.[292] This provides the first binding
legal framework for safeguarding both the iboga plant and
the traditional knowledge associated with it. In simple terms,
it means that iboga providers operating from countries par-
ticipating in the Nagoya protocol (such as Brazil, Mexico, or
Costa Rica) may be legally obliged to provide documentation proving the non-Gabonese origin of the ibogaine they
use. Exceptions to this rule exist in cases where the Gabonese
Ministry of Culture has given express permission to export
iboga. This permission remains available to serious researchers engaged in projects that benefit traditional knowledge
holders and/or the public interest.

2015 USA: In order to address the growing impact of the U.S. Opioid crisis in their home states, politicians from Vermont and New York implement bills H741 and A5459 respectively.[293, 294] Both these bills are aimed at legalizing ibogaine for the treatment of addiction.

2018 Maryland: Lawmakers begin discussing ibogaine's potential to curb its opioid problem.[295]

2019 California: On Tuesday, June 4th, 2019, Oakland's city council unanimously passed a resolution to decriminalize the use of natural psychedelics, including mushrooms, cacti, and iboga.[296]

2020 Ann Arbor, Michigan, Santa Cruz, California, and Washington DC decriminalize iboga.

2020: Researchers led by David Olson, a chemical neuroscientist at the University of California, report engineering a non-toxic and non-hallucinogenic chemical cousin of ibogaine that alleviates depression and addictive behaviors in rodents. They name the compound 'tabernanthalog,' or TBG.[297]

2021: MINDCURE, a Canadian technology company, announced it had begun the first stage of manufacturing pharmaceutical grade ibogaine to be used in clinical research.[298]

THE END

SELECTED BIBLIOGRAPHY

Alexander, Bruce. K. *The Globalization of Addiction: A Study in Poverty of the Spirit*. Oxford University Press. 2008.

Eliade, Mircea. *Archaic Techniques of Ecstasy*. Librarie Payot, 1951.

Fernandez, James W. Bwiti: *An Ethnography of the Religious Imagination in Africa*. Princeton University Press. 1982.

Fernandez. James W. Tabernanthe Iboga. *Ecstasis and the work of the ancestors. Essay published in Flesh of the Gods. The ritual use of Hallucinogens*. Edited by Peter T Furst. Waveland Pr Inc, 1990.

Grof, Stanislav. *Beyond the Brain: Birth, Death, and Transcendence in Psychotherapy*. SUNY Press, 1983.

Grof, Stanislav. *The Adventure of Self-Discovery: Dimensions of Consciousness and New Perspectives in Psychotherapy and Inner Exploration*. SUNY Press, 1988.

Grof, Stanislav. Zina Bennett, Hal. *The Holotropic Mind: The Three Levels of Human Consciousness and How They Shape Our Lives*. HarperOne, 1993.

Huxley, Aldous. *Doors of Perception,* Harper and Row, 1954,

James, William. *Varieties of Religious Experience.* Longmans, Green & Co, 1902.

Campbell, Joseph. *The Power of Myth.* 1988.

Jung. Carl, G. *Letters of C. G. Jung, Volume 2*; Volumes 1951-1961.

Lotsof, Howard. *Ibogaine Patients Bill of Rights.*

McKenna, Terence. *Food of the Gods: The Search for the Original Tree of Knowledge – A Radical History of Plants, Drugs, and Human Evolution.* New York, Bantam. 1992.

Mate, Gabor. *In the Realm of Hungry Ghosts: Close Encounters with Addiction.* North Atlantic Books, 2010.

Naranjo, Claudio. *The Healing Journey.* Pantheon Books, 1974.

Pollan, Michael. *How to Change your Mind. What the New Science of Psychedelics Teaches Us About Consciousness, Dying, Addiction, Depression, and Transcendence.* Penguin Press, 2018.

Ravalec V, Mallendi, Paicheler A. *Iboga:The Visionary Root of African Shamanism.* Park Street Press, 2007.

Shanon, Benny. The Antipodes of the Mind: Charting the Phenomenology of the Ayahuasca Experience. Oxford University Press. 2002.

Terence, Mckenna. *The Archaic Revival: Speculations on Psychedelic Mushrooms, the Amazon, Virtual Reality, UFOs, Evolution,*

Shamanism, the Rebirth of the Goddess, and the End of History. HarperCollins, 1992.

Talbot, Michael. The Holographic Universe: The Revolutionary Theory of Reality. 1991, Harper Perennial.

Watts, Alan. *The Two Hands Of God: The Myths Of Polarity.* George Bazilier,1963.

Dickinson, Jonathan. McAlpin, Jamie R.N. Wilkins, Clare. Fitz-simmons, Christine R.N. Paige, Guion R.N. Paterson, Tanea. Greene, Douglas. Chaves, Bruno Rasmussen M.D. Editors. Kamlet, Jeffrey M.D., DABAM, FASAM. Paskulin, Roman M.D., Ph.D. September 2015. *Clinical Guidelines for Ibogaine-Assisted Detoxification* - The Global Ibogaine Therapy Alliance.

ONLINE RESOURCES

www.ibogainealliance.org

www.MAPS.org/ibogaine-therapy

www.blessingsoftheforest.org

www.Ibogatherapy.com

www.psychedelicsinrecovery.org

www.ceibaibogaine.com

www.zappyzapolin.com

www.ebando.org

Ibogaine Universe Facebook Page: www.facebook.com/groups/diboga4

www.ibogaine.co.uk

www.myeboga.com

NOTES

WHAT IS IBOGA?

1 Terence, Mckenna. *The Archaic Revival: Speculations on Psychedelic Mushrooms, the Amazon, Virtual Reality, UFOs, Evolution, Shamanism, the Rebirth of the Goddess, and the End of History.* HarperCollins, 1992, p.45.

2 Pinchbeck, Daniel. *Daniel Pinchbeck's account of Bwiti initiation in Gabon,* 1999, http://www.ibogaine.co.uk/exp5.htm#. WIYl1FMrLIU, retrieved October 4, 2017

3 Ravalec V, Mallendi, Paicheler A. *Iboga: The Visionary Root of African Shamanism*, Park Street Press, 2007, p.6.

4 McGown, Jay. *"Out of Africa: Mysteries of Access and Benefit Sharing,"* 2006. http://www.theopenunderground.de/@pdf/ kapital/fairtreten/outofafrica.pdf. Retrieved July 7, 2018

5 Widerski. S: La religion bouiti – NY, Ottawa, Toronto, éd. Legas, pages 685-687. Taken from: *Approche thérapeutique de la prise d'iboga dans l'initiation au Bwiti vécue par les Occidentaux.* Retrieved August 16 2018 from: https://www. cairn.info/revue-psychotropes-2004-3-page-51.htm

6 Fernandez, James W. *Bwiti: An Ethnography of the Religious Imagination in Africa.* Princeton University Press; 1982, P321-322

7 Julian Oliver Caldecott and Lera Miles. *World Atlas of Great Apes and Their Conservation.* 2005, p116

8 William A. Haviland, Harald E. L. Prins, Dana Walrath, Bunny McBride. *The Essence of Anthropology 3rd edition.* Cengage Learning, 2012 p. 17

9 Hanly, Elizabeth. June 18, 2004). "Listening To Koko."
https://www.commonwealmagazine.org/listening-koko
Retrieved January 10, 2018

10 Julian Oliver Caldecott and Lera Miles, *World Atlas of Great Apes and Their Conservation*, 2005, p116

11 Adams, Douglas. *The Hitchhiker's Guide to the Galaxy*. Del Rey; Reissue edition, 1995, P. 61

12 http://www.foxnews.com/health/2015/04/01/african-plant-outlawed-in-us-may-offer-treatment-for-addicts.html

13 http://www.rollingstone.com/culture/features/how-doc-tors-treat-mental-illness-with-psychedelic-drugs-w470673

THE PREPARATIONS

14 Popik P, Skolnick P. *Pharmacology of ibogaine and ibo-gaine-related alkaloids.*In: Cordell GA, ed. The Alkaloids. Vol. 52. San Diego, CA: Academic Press; 1998:197-231

15 Houck, Max M. *Forensic Chemistry* - Elsevier Science. P.164

16 Michael H. Baumann, John Pablo, Syed F. Ali, Richard B. Rothman, Deborah C. Mash. *Comparative Neuropharmacol-ogy of Ibogaine and its O-Desmethyl Metabolite, Noribogaine.* The Alkaloids, Vol. 56. 2001, P 79-1137

17 Pearl, S. M.; Herrick-Davis, K.; Teitler, M.; Glick, S. D. (Mar 27, 1995). *"Radioligand-binding study of noribogaine, a likely metabolite of ibogaine".Brain Research.* 675 (1-2): PDF Retrieved March 10 from: https://www.ncbi.nlm.nih.gov/pubmed/7796150

THE JOURNEY

18 https://www.ibogainealliance.org/guidelines/dosing.

19 Mckenna, Terence. *"Alien Dreamtime,"* a multimedia event recorded live. (27 February 1993) https://www.youtube.com/watch?v=_86NhPx0hZQ

20 Marcus, Aubrey. Interview with Joe Rogan. Feb 18, 2013, https://www.youtube.com/watch?v=rJNlPfElDIs

21 G. Roberts and J. Owen, Br. J. Psychiatry. 153, 607 (1988). Taken from Alper, Kenneth R. *IBOGAINE: A REVIEW*. Departments of Psychiatry and Neurology. New York University School of Medicine. New York, NY 10016: PDF Retrieved June 10, 2017

22 Dickinson, Jonathan. McAlpin, Jamie R.N. Wilkins, Clare. Fitzsimmons, Christine R.N. Paige, Guion R.N. Paterson, Tanea. Greene, Douglas. Chaves, Bruno Rasmussen M.D. Editors. Kamlet, Jeffrey M.D., DABAM, FASAM. Paskulin, Roman M.D., Ph.D. September 2015. Clinical *Guidelines for Ibogaine-Assisted Detoxification - The Global Ibogaine Therapy Alliance*. PDF Retrieved February 22, 2018, from https://www.ibogainealliance.org/guidelines/

THE DREAM MACHINE

23 James, William. *Varieties of Religious Experience*. Longmans, Green & Co, 1902, P, 378-9

24 Leary, Timothy; Metzner, Ralph; Alpert, Richard. *The Psychedelic Experience. A Manual Based on the Tibetan Book of the Dead*. Citadel, 1964 P. 5

25 White, Richard. *The Heart of Wisdom: A Philosophy of Spiritual Life*, Rowman & Littlefield, 2012, P. 7

26 Shanon, Benny. *The Antipodes of the Mind: Charting the Phenomenology of the Ayahuasca Experience*, Oxford University Press; 2002,

27 Author Interview with Bwiti practitioner

28 Castaneda, Carlos. *A Separate Reality*, New York, Simon & Schuster. P.121

29 Lan, EJ. Sugihara, I. Llinas, R. *Differential roles of apamin- and charybdotoxin- sensitive K+ conductances in the generation*

of inferior olive rhythmicity in vivo. J Neurosci (1997 Apr 15) 17(8):2825-38. Retrieved September 15 from The Bulletin of the Multidisciplinary Association for Psychedelic Studies MAPS - Volume 8 Number 1 Spring 1998 - pp. 5-14

30 Anderson, C.M. *Ibogaine Therapy in Chemical Dependency and Posttraumatic Stress Disorder: A Hypothesis Involving the Fractal Nature of Fetal REM Sleep and Interhemispheric Reintegration.* Retrieved September 13, 2018, from http://www.maps.org/news-letters/v08n1/08105and.html

31 http://www.britannica.com/EBchecked/topic/287907/information-theory/214958/Physiology

32 IBID

33 Huxley, Aldous. *Doors of Perception,* Harper and Row, 1954, P.6

34 IBID

35 Jung, Carl. G. *Mysterium Coniunctionis, Collected Works,* Vol 14, par. 778

36 Carhartt Harris, Robin. Taken from Pollan, Michael. *How to Change your Mind. What the New Science of Psychedelics Teaches Us About Consciousness, Dying, Addiction, Depression, and Transcendence.* Penguin Press. 2018 P.315

37 IBID P. 300, 301

38 Raichle, Marcus. Taken from Pollan, Michael. *How to Change your Mind. What the New Science of Psychedelics Teaches Us About Consciousness, Dying, Addiction, Depression, and Transcendence.* 2018. Penguin Press. P.303

39 IBID

40 IBID

41 Pollan, Michael. *How to Change your Mind. What the New Science of Psychedelics Teaches Us About Consciousness, Dying, Addiction, Depression, and Transcendence.* 2018. Penguin Press. P.313

42 Carhartt Harris, Robin. *Taken from Pollan, Michael. How to Change your Mind. What the New Science of Psychedelics Teaches Us About Consciousness, Dying, Addiction, Depression, and Transcendence.* 2018. Penguin Press. 304

43 IBID

44 Huxley, Aldous. *Heaven and Hell.* Harper & Bros, 1956, P. 2

45 Fernandez. James W *Tabernanthe Iboga. Ecstasis and the work of the ancestors,* Essay published in Flesh of the Gods. The ritual use of Hallucinogens. Edited by Peter T Furst. Waveland Pr Inc. 1990 P 258

46 Carhartt Harris, Robin. Taken from Pollan, Michael. *How to Change your Mind. What the New Science of Psychedelics Teaches Us About Consciousness, Dying, Addiction, Depression, and Transcendence.* 2018. Penguin Press. P.305, 306

47 Fernandez. James W Tabernanthe Iboga. *Ecstasis and the work of the ancestors,* Essay published in Flesh of the Gods. The ritual use of Hallucinogens. Edited by Peter T Furst. Waveland Pr Inc. 1990 P 241

48 McKenna, Terence. *Food of the Gods: The Search for the Original Tree of Knowledge – A Radical History of Plants, Drugs, and Human Evolution.* New York: Bantam. 1992. P.12

THE PSYCHOTHERAPIST

49 The Guardian. September 20, 2003. *"Ten Years of Therapy in one Night."* Retrieved November 4 2017 from: https://www.theguardian.com/books/2003/sep/20/booksonhealth.lifeandhealth.

50 Sacks, Oliver. August 2012. *Altered States: Self-experiments in chemistry.* Retrieved January 26 from https://www.newyorker.com/magazine/2012/08/27/altered-states-3

51 Hofmann Dr. Albert, in the Foreword to LSD: My Problem Child. 2009 MAPS.org; 4th edition

52 https://www.samharris.org/podcast/item/drugs-and-the-meaning-of-life. Retrieved January 16, 2019

53 Jung. Carl, G. Letters of C. G. Jung, Volume 2; Volumes 1951-1961. P.172

54 IBID P.222

55 Z. Binienda, M.A. Beaudoin, B.T. Thorn, D.R. Papurna, R.A. Johnson, C.M. Fogle, W. Jr. Slikker, and S.F. Ali, Ann. N. Y. Acad. Sci. 844, 265 (1998 191. H. Depoortere, Neuro-psychobiology 18, 160 (1987). Taken from Alper K (2001): Ibogaine: a review. In: Alper KR, Proceedings of the first international conference. P. 1-38.

56 Naranjo, Claudio. *The Healing Journey.*Pantheon Books; 1974. P.214

57 IBID P.214

58 IBID P.176

59 IBID P.215

60 IBID P.216

61 IBID P.203

62 Mash, Deborah C. (2000) *Ibogaine: Complex Pharma-cokinetics, Concerns for Safety, and Preliminary Efficacy Measures.* Annals of the New York Academy of Sciences. Retrieved June 10, 2018, from https://www.ncbi.nlm.nih.gov/pubmed/11085338

63 Bastiaans, Ehud. Supervisor: Prof. Dr. C. Kaplan. November 2004 *Life after Ibogaine: An exploratory study of the long-term effects of ibogaine treatment on drug addicts.* PDF Retrieved February 11 2018 from: https://www.iceers.org/docs/science/iboga/Bastiaans%20E_Life_After_Ibogaine.pdf

WHAT IBOGAINE CAN DO

64 Mike Tyson on smoking DMT: *Do you understand the toad?* The Art of Conversation w/ Dan Le Batard, ESPN,

https://www.youtube.com/watch? v=jYcnaYEzX7Y

65 Taub, Benjamin. *Treating addiction with psychedelics – part 2: preparation.* Taken from: https://thethirdwave.co/ treat-addiction-psychedelics-preparation/

66 Johnson, Matt, P.h.D. Taken from Pollan, *Michael. How to Change your Mind. What the New Science of Psychedelics Teaches Us About Consciousness, Dying, Addiction, Depression, and Transcendence.* 2018. Penguin Press. P.366

67 K.K. Szumlinski and I.M. Maisonneuve, Toxicon 39, 75 (2001) retrieved from Alper, Iceers 2012

68 E. Hennevin, B. Hars, C. Maho, and V. Bloch, Behav. Brain. Res. 69, 125 (1995). 193. M. Jouvet, J. Sleep Res. 7, 1 (1998). Retrieved from Alper ICEERS

69 R. Goutarel, O. Gollnhofer, and R. Sillans, Psyched. Mono. Essays 6, 70 (1993). Taken from ICEERS 2012 Alper

70 Baumann MH, Pablo J, Ali SF, Rothman RB, Mash DC (2001). *Comparative neuropharmacology of ibogaine and its O-desmethyl metabolite, noribogaine. The Alkaloids: Chemistry and Biology.* P. 56

WHAT IBOGAINE CAN'T DO

71 Metzner, Ralph. *Green Psychology: Transforming Our Relationship to the Earth.* Park Street Press. 1999

72 Walsh, Roger. *Altered Traits: Science Reveals How Meditation Changes Your Mind, Brain, and Body,* 2017, Avery

AFTERCARE

73 Jung. Carl, G. *Letter to Bill Wilson.*

74 IBID

75 IBID

76 Mcnamara, Patrick. *The Neuroscience of Religious Experience.* 2009 Cambridge University Press.

77 Grof, Stanislav. *The Adventure of Self-Discovery: Dimensions of Consciousness and New Perspectives in Psychotherapy and Inner Exploration*, SUNY Press, 1988, p. 268.

WHY THE PAIN?

78 De Quincey, Thomas. *Confessions of an English Opium Eater*, A. & C. Black, 1863, p. 11

79 Chauvet C, Lardeux V, Goldberg SR, Jaber M, Solinas M. *Environmental enrichment reduces cocaine seeking and reinstatement induced by cues and stress but not by cocaine.* Neuropsychopharmacology. 2009 34(13):2767-78. doi: 10.1038/npp.2009.127. https://www.ncbi.nlm.nih.gov/ pubmed/19741591, Retrieved April 22, 2018

80 Zinberg, Norman. *Drug, Set, And Setting:The Basis For Controlled Intoxicant Use Yale University Press*, 1986, pp. X–xi

81 https://twitter.com/SecPriceMD/sta-tus/906156067754831873, Retrieved November 25 2017

82 National Drug Threat Assessment Summary", DEA, 2015 https://www.dea.gov/docs/2015%20NDTA%20Report.pdf, Retrieved September 20, 2017

83 Associated Press. *Drug overdoses now kill more Americans than guns*, 2016, https://www.cbsnews.com/news/drug-overdose-deaths-heroin-opioid-prescription-painkillers-more-than-guns/. Retrieved September 20, 2017

84 Katz, Josh. *Drug Deaths in America Are Rising Faster Than Ever*, June 2017, https://www.nytimes.com/interactive/2017/06/05/ upshot/opioid-epidemic-drug-overdose-deaths-are-rising-fast-er-than-ever.html?_r=0. Retrieved October 5, 2017

85 Mate, Gabor. *In the Realm of Hungry Ghosts*, 2010 North Atlantic Books.

86 Mash, Deborah. *Dr. Deborah Mash on Why Ibogaine Treatment Aftercare is Key to Treating the Roots of Addiction.*

April 4, 2016, https://psychedelictimes.com/iboga/dr-debo-rah-mash-on-why-ibogaine-treatment-aftercare-is-key-to-treating-the-roots-of-addiction, Retrieved June 12, 2017

87 IBID

88 IBID

89 Alexander, Bruce. K. *The Globalization of Addiction: A Study in Poverty of the Spirit.* Oxford University Press. 2008. *P:35*

90 IBID P.29

91 IBID P.35

92 IBID P.59

93 Alexander, Bruce. K. *Addiction, Environmental Crisis, and Global Capitalism* http://www.brucekalexander.com/articles-speeches/ecological-issues/addiction,-environmen-tal-crisis,-and-global-capitalism Retrieved March 4, 2018

94 Alexander, Bruce. K. *Addiction as Seen from the Perspective of Karl Polanyi* http://www.brucekalexander.com/articles-speeches/dislocation-theory-addiction/215-addic-tionseenfromkarlpolanyi- Retrieved March 10, 2018

95 Mate, Gabor. *In the Realm of Hungry Ghosts: Close Encounters with Addiction.* North Atlantic Books. 2010. P261

96 Alexander, Bruce. K. *The Roots of Addiction in Free Market Society* http://www.brucekalexander.com/articles-speeches/dislocation-theory-addiction/201-the-rootsofaddictionin-freemarketsociety Retrieved March 3, 2018

97 Alexander, Bruce. K. *Bruce K. Alexander on addiction and the imagination.* https://www.robhopkins.net/2017/06/27/bruce-k-alexander-on-addiction-and-the-imagination/ Retrieved February 10, 2018

98 Alexander, Bruce. K. *Addiction: The View from Rat Park (2010)* http://www.brucekalexander.com/articles-speeches/rat-park/148-addiction-the-view-from-rat-park Retrieved March 12, 2018

THE WAR ON DRUGS BEGINS

99 Alexander, Bruce. K. *Healing Addiction Through Community: A Much Longer Road Than it Seems?*

100 Loewen. James. W. *Lies My Teacher Told Me: Everything Your American History Textbook Got Wrong.* The New Press. 1995. P.95

101 Reichel-Dolmatoff 1975, p. 48. As cited in Soibelman, T. *My Father and My Mother, Show Me Your Beauty: Ritual Use of Ayahuasca in Rio de Janeiro.* 1995, p. 14

102 Rudgley, Richard. *The Encyclopedia of Psychoactive Substances.* New York City: 1998

103 Juan de Cárdenas 1. *Problemas y secretos maravillosos de las Indias.* Alianza Editorial, Madrid.1988

104 Guerra, F. *The Pre-Columbian Mind.* Seminar Press, London. 1971

BWITI AND IBOGA – REMEMBERING DISMEMBERMENT

105 Stafford, P. (1992). *Psychedelics Encyclopedia,* 3rd ed., Ronin Publishing, Berkeley, P. 104.

106 From words by Nengue Me Ndjoung Isidore, ecumenical Bwiti religious leader, and magistrate in the Libreville Supreme Court, quoted in Swiderski 1990-91, vol. I: 628. Taken from Samorini, Giorgio, *The Bwiti Religion and the psychoactive plant Tabernanthe iboga* (Equatorial Africa) https://ibogainedossier.com/samorini.html

107 John L. Wilson. *Visit to the Upper Waters of the Gabon,* The Missionary Herald. 39 (June 1843):238. Taken from Fernandez, James W. Bwiti: An Ethnography of the Religious Imagination in Africa . Princeton University Press; 1982, P 30

108 IBID

109 Fernandez, James W. *Bwiti: An Ethnography of the Religious Imagination in Africa.* Princeton University Press; 1982, P 275

110 Du Bellay, Le Gabon," p. 310 Taken from Fernandez, James W. Bwiti: *An Ethnography of the Religious Imagination in Africa.* Princeton University Press; 1982, P 36

111 Fernandez James W. *Tabernanthe Iboga. Ecstasis and the work of the ancestors.* Essay published in *Flesh of the Gods. The ritual use of Hallucinogens.* Edited by Peter T Furst. Waveland Pr Inc. 1990. P245

112 Ravalec V, Mallendi, Paicheler A. *Iboga: The Visionary Root of African Shamanism,* Park Street Press, 2007, P. 19

113 André Mary Le défi du syncrétisme. *Le travail symbolique de la religion d'Eboga* (Gabon). Paris, EHESS, 1999 Taken from *Iboga, The visionary root of African shamanism.* Ravalec V, Mallendi, Paicheler A.Iboga, Park Street Press , 2007.

114 Amorini, Giorgio. *The Bwiti Religion and the psychoactive plant Tabernanthe iboga* (Equatorial Africa) https://ibogainedossier.com/samorini.html

115 IBID

116 IBID

117 Kingsley, Mary. *Travels,* pp. 429-430 Taken from Fernandez, James W. *Bwiti: An Ethnography of the Religious Imagination in Africa.* Princeton University Press; 1982, P 38

118 Tonye, Mahop Marcelin. Asaha, Stella, Dr. NDAM Nouhou. Blackmore, Paul. March 2000. *State of knowledge study on Tabernanthe Iboga Baillon. A report for the Central African regional program for the environment.* PDF Retrieved December 10 2020 from http://www.mindvox.com/pipermail/ibogaine/attachments/20120305/4922f9cb/attachment-0001.pdf

119 http://www.bbc.co.uk/programmes/b007ly82

THE WAY BACK PLAYBACK

120 Watts, Alan. *The Two Hands Of God: The Myths Of Polarity*. George Bazilier. 1963. P.46

121 Time's arrow: Albert Einstein's letters to Michele Besso. https://www.christies.com/features/Einstein-letters-to-Michele-Besso-8422-1.aspx Retrieved 1 January 2021

122 Wilcock, David. *The Source Field Investigations*, Penguin Group, 2011, p. 56.

123 Sand. Nicholas. *Journey into the Realm of Ibogaine*. The entheogen review, pob 19820, sacramento, ca 95819-0820, usavolume xi, number 3autumnal equinox 2002. Retrieved December 2017 from: http://www.serendipity.li/dmt/ibogaine.pdf

124 Eliade, Mircea. *Archaic Techniques of Ecstasy*, Librarie Payot, 1951, p. 103.

125 http://reset.me/personal-story/psycho-spiritual-iboga-experience. October 15, 2014, Retrieved 18th June 2017

126 Dolmatoff, Reichel. *The shaman and the Jaguar. A study of narcotic drugs among the Indians of Columbia* Temple University Press, 1975. Taken from: Shanon, Benny. *The Antipodes of the Mind: Charting the Phenomenology of the Ayahuasca Experience*, Oxford University Press; 2002, p. 130

127 Author Interview with Bwiti member.

128 Shanon, Benny. *The Antipodes of the Mind: Charting the Phenomenology of the Ayahuasca Experience*, Oxford University Press; 2002, p. 129

129 IBID p.151

130 IBID p.240

131 IBID p.231

132 Harari, Yuval. Noah. (2016). Homo deus: A brief history of tomorrow. Harvill Secker. 2015 P181

133 Time's arrow: Albert Einstein's letters to Michele Besso. https://www.christies.com/features/Einstein-letters-to-Michele-Besso-8422-1.aspx Retrieved 1 January 2021

134 Carhartt Harris, Robin. Taken from Pollan, *Michael. How to Change your Mind. What the New Science of Psychedelics Teaches Us About Consciousness, Dying, Addiction, Depression, and Transcendence.* 2018. Penguin Press. P.313

135 Rudd M, Vohs KD, Aaker J. *Awe expands people's perception of time, alters decision making, and enhances well-being.* http://assets.csom.umn.edu/assets/lib/assets/AssetLibrary/2012/Rudd_Vohs_Aaker_2012_psyc h_pdf, Retrieved July 5, 2018

136 Shanon, Benny. *The Antipodes of the Mind: Charting the Phenomenology of the Ayahuasca Experience,* Oxford University Press; 2002, p. 235

137 IBID p. 236

138 Grof, Stanislav. *Beyond the Brain: Birth, Death, and Transcendence in Psychotherapy,* SUNY Press, 1983, p. 33.

139 Joseph Campbell, *The Power of Myth* (1988) with Bill Moyers, Episode 2

140 Grof, Stanislav. *The Adventure of Self-Discovery: Dimensions of Consciousness and New Perspectives in Psychotherapy and Inner Exploration,* SUNY Press, 1988, p, 99.

141 IBID

142 IBID

143 Brown, David Jay. *Frontiers of Psychedelic Consciousness: Conversations with Albert Hofmann, Stanislav Grof, Rick Strassman, Jeremy Narby, Simon Posford, and Others,* Park St Press, 2015, pp 18-44

144 IBID

145 IBID

146 Talbot, Michael. *The Holographic Universe: The Revolutionary Theory of Reality,* 1991, Harper Perennial, p. 53.

147 Eccles, John. *The Reach of the Mind: Nobel Prize Conversations*, Saybrook Publishing Co, 1985, p. 91. Retrieved from The *Holographic Universe*

148 Andrew A. M. (1997). *The decade of the brain - further thoughts*. p. 255–264. https://www.researchgate.net/publication/235266973_The_decade_of_the_brain_-_further_thoughts Retrieved July 18 2018

149 F. David Peat. *Infinite Potential: The Life and Times of David Bohm*, Addison Wesley, 1997, pp. 316-31

150 Calaprice. Alice. *The New Quotable Einstein*, Princeton University Press, 2005 p. 206.

151 Shanon, Benny. *The Antipodes of the Mind: Charting the Phenomenology of the Ayahuasca Experience*, Oxford University Press; 2002, p.236

152 Blake, William. *The Marriage of Heaven and Hell*, p. 14.

153 Sinnett, Alfred Percy (1884) *Esoteric Buddhism (5th ed.)* Houghton Mifflin.

154 Underhill, Evelyn. Mysticism: *A Study of the Nature and Development of Man's Spiritual Consciousness*, 1911, p.154

155 Bailey, Alice. A. *Light of the Soul on The Yoga Sutras of Patanjali – Book 3 – Union achieved and its Results* (1927) P.276

156 Jung, Carl Gustav. *Two Essays on Analytical Psychology, Volume 7, The Collected Works of C. G. Jung*, Princeton University Press, 1966

157 Jung, Carl Gustav. *The Significance of Constitution and Heredity in Psychology Collected Works vol. 8*, 1929, p, 112.

158 Jung, Carl Gustav. *Conscious, Unconscious, and Individuation*, 1939, 518 pp. 286, 287.

159 Bailey, Alice. A. *Light of the Soul on The Yoga Sutras of Patanjali – Book 3 – Union achieved and its Results* (1927) P.276

160 IBID

161 Heinlein, Robert. A. *In Time Enough for Love: The Lives of Lazarus Long,* G.P. Putnam's Sons, 1973, p. 250.

162 Clarke, Arthur C. *Profiles of the Future: An Inquiry into the Limits of the Possible.* Popular Library, 1973

IF SO, SO WHAT?

163 Watts, Alan. *The Two Hands Of God: The Myths Of Polarity.* George Bazilier. 1963. P.46

164 Sand. Nicholas. *Journey into the Realm of Ibogaine.* The entheogen review, pob 19820, sacramento, ca 95819-0820, usavolume xi, number 3autumnal equinox 2002. Retrieved December 2017 from: http://www.serendipity.li/dmt/ibogaine.pdf

165 Thomas Taylor- *The Eleusinian and Bacchic Mysteries.* Kessinger Publishing. 1993. P120

166 Quinn, Daniel. *The Story of B.* New York. Bantam Books. 1996, P.307

167 McKenna, Terence. *Food of the Gods: The Search for the Original Tree of Knowledge – A Radical History of Plants, Drugs, and Human Evolution.* New York: Bantam. 1992. P.57

168 Eliade, Mircea. *Archaic Techniques of Ecstasy.* 1951. P. 143

169 James Rodger. *Understanding the Healing Potential of Ibogaine through a Comparative and Interpretive Phenomenology of the Visionary Experience.* Retrieved January 15 from https://anthrosource.onlinelibrary.wiley.com/doi/full/10.1111/anoc.12088

170 Samorini, George. *Adam, Eve, and Iboga* , 1993, http://www.samorini.it/doc1/sam/sam-1993-adam.pdf, Retrieved December 15, 2017

171 Fernandez, James W. *Bwiti: An Ethnography of the Religious Imagination in Africa,* Princeton University Press, 1982, p. 71.

172 Taussig, Michael. *Shamanism, Colonialism, and the Wild Man: A Study in Terror and Healing,* University of Chicago Press, 1987

173 Nicholas Thomas, Caroline Humphrey. *Shamanism, History, and the State,* University of Michigan Press, 1996, p.104.

174 Joseph Campbell, *The Power of Myth* (1988) with Bill Moyers, Episode 2

175 Warren, Jeff. *Tourists of Consciousness.* Retrieved January 2018 from http://jeffwarren.org/uncategorized/touristsofconsciousness/

176 Fernandez, James W. Bwiti: *An Ethnography of the Religious Imagination in Africa,* Princeton University Press, 1982, p.490–491

177 Narby, Jeremy. *Intelligence in Nature: An Inquiry into Knowledge,* Penguin Books, 2006.

178 Warren, Jeff. May 27, 2009, *Tourists of Consciousness.* http://jeffwarren.org/uncategorized/touristsofconsciousness, Retrieved June 10, 2018

CONCLUSION

179 McKenna, Terence. Food of the Gods: The Search for the Original Tree of Knowledge – A Radical History of Plants, Drugs, and Human Evolution. New York: Bantam. 1992. P139

180 Deaton, Angus. Case, Anne.*Rising morbidity and mortality in midlife among white non-Hispanic Americans in the 21st century.* PDF retrieved from http://www.pnas.org/content/pnas/early/2015/10/29/1518393112.full.pdf on 5/8/2018

181 Underhill, Evelyn. *Practical Mysticism.* 1915. Preface.

THE MONEY TREE: IBOGA SUSTAINABILITY
AND CONSERVATION

182 Alper KR, Lotsof HS, Kaplan CD. *The ibogaine medical subculture.* J Ethnopharmacol. 2008;115(1) pp, 9-24.

183 https://www.ibogainealliance.org/files/GITA-Durban-2014-Event-Summary.pdf. Retrieved May 20 2019

THE LIFE COACH: MICRODOSING WITH IBOGA

184 Huxley, Aldous. *The Doors of Perception.* P.16 1954

185 Kotler, Steven. *The Rise of Superman: Decoding the Science of Ultimate Human Performance.* New Harvest, March 2014

THE PHYSICIAN: BOGA AND PHYSICAL HEALING

186 Lotsof, Howard S. *"Compositions for the treatment of hepatitis c and methods for using compositions for the treatment of hepatitis c."* US Patent Application EP 2083825 A1. September 2006. Retrieved February 5, 2018 from https://www.google.com/patents/EP2083825A1?cl=en

187 IBID

188 Jankovic J (April 2008). *"Parkinson's disease: clinical features and diagnosis".* Journal of Neurology, Neurosurgery, and Psychiatry. 79 (4): 368–76.

189 Sveinbjornsdottir, S (11 July 2016). *"The clinical symptoms of Parkinson's disease.".* Journal of Neurochemistry. 139: 318–324.

190 https://www.ninds.nih.gov/Disorders/All-Disorders/Parkinsons-Disease-Information-Page

191 Carnicella, S., He, D.Y., Yowell, Q.V., Glick, S.D., Ron, D. *"Noribogaine, but not 18-MC, exhibits similar actions as ibogaine on GDNF expression and ethanol self-administration."* Addiction Biology. October 2010.

192 Gill, S. S., Patel, N. K., Hotton, G. R., O'Sullivan, McCarter, R., Bunnage, M., Brooks, D. J., Svendsen, C. N. and Heywood, P. (2003) *"Direct brain infusion of glial cell-line*

derived neurotrophic factor in Parkinson's disease." Nature Medicine, 9, 589-595

193 NINDS Multiple Sclerosis Information Page. National Institute of Neurological Disorders and Stroke. November 19, 2015.

194 NINDS Multiple Sclerosis Information Page. National Institute of Neurological Disorders and Stroke. November 19, 2015.

195 Compositions and methods for treating multiple sclerosis https://www.google.com/patents/US20110195049 P.10

196 Ngian GS, Guymer EK, Littlejohn GO (February 2011). *"The use of opioids in fibromyalgia".* Int J Rheum Dis. 14 (1):Pat 6–11

IBOGAINE RELATED FATALITIES

197 H.I. Dhahir, *A Comparative Study of the Toxicity of Ibogaine and Serotonin.* Doctoral Thesis, 71-25-341, University Microfilm International, Ann Arbor, MI, 1971. Taken from ICEERS PDF. Kenneth R. Alper, M.D., Howard S. Lotsof, Geerte M. N. Frenken, M.F.A., Daniel J. Luciano, M.D., Jan Bastiaans, M.D. *Treatment of Acute Opioid Withdrawal with Ibogaine.* The American Journal on Addictions 8:234–242,1999 American Academy of Addiction Psychiatry

198 Alper K, Stajić M, Gill JR. *Fatalities temporally associated with the ingestion of ibogaine.* J Forensic Sci. 2012 Mar;57(2):398-412. doi: 10.1111/j.1556-4029.2011.02008.x. Epub 2012 Jan 23.

199 Hannaford, Alex. (Dec 2017) *"Dying to get clean: is ibogaine the answer to heroin addiction?"* Retrieved Jun10 2018 from: https://www.theguardian.com/society/2017/dec/10/ibogaine-heroin-addiction-treatment-gabon-withdrawal-danger-death

200 Lindsay Murdoch. (19 December 2014) *"Western Australian Brodie Smith's bid for ibogaine drug cure ends in death."* Retrieved Jun12 2018 from http://www.smh.com.au/national/western-australian-brodie-smiths-bid-for-ibogaine-drug-cure-ends-in-death-20141216-1283pk.html,

201 Critchley, Graeme. (20th November 2016) *"Deadly pill peril: Illegal killer drug freely available online."* Retrieved Jun10 2018 from: https://www.dailystar.co.uk/news/latest-news/563403/illegal-pills-Ibogaine-drug-addicts-sold-online

IBOGA/IBOGAINE PHYSICAL EFFECTS

202 https://www.ibogainealliance.org/guidelines/patient-criteria-considerations/

THE SUCCESS RATE OF IBOGAINE

203 Alper, Lotsof, Fremken, Luciano, and Bastiaans, 1999. Evidence from clinical studies. Complete resolution of withdrawal symptoms in 29 of 33 subjects, (8): 234-242)

204 Davis, Alan. K, Barsuglia, Joseph. P, Austin-Marley-Windham-Herman, Lynch, Marta. Polanco, Martin. October 17, 2017 *"Subjective effectiveness of ibogaine treatment for problematic opioid consumption: Short- and long-term outcomes and current psychological functioning"*. Journal of Psychedelic Studies 1(2), pp. 65–73 (2017) DOI: 10.1556/2054.01.2017.009. Retrieved 18 July 2018 from http://akademiai.com/doi/pdf/10.1556/2054.01.2017.009

205 IBID

IBOGA/IBOGAINE CONTRAINDICATIONS

206 https://www.ibogainealliance.org/guidelines/
207 Cuculi F, Kobza R, Ehmann T, Erne P. *ECG changes*

amongst patients with alcohol withdrawal seizures and delirium tremens. Swiss Med Wkly 2006;136(13–14):223–7. Taken from Alper, Kenneth R. IBOGAINE: A REVIEW. Departments of Psychiatry and Neurology. New York University School of Medicine. New York, NY 10016: PDF Retrieved June 10, 2017

208 A.H. Rezvani, D.H. Overstreet, Y. Yang, I.M. Maisonneuve, U.K. Bandarage, M.E. Kuehne, and S.D. Glick, *Attenuation of alcohol consumption by a novel nontoxic ibogaine analogue (18-methoxycoronaridine) in alcohol-preferring rats.* Pharmacol. Biochem. Behav. 58, 615/ Taken from Alper, Kenneth R. IBOGAINE: A REVIEW. Departments of Psychiatry and Neurology. New York University School of Medicine. New York, NY 10016: PDF Retrieved June 10 2017

209 S.D. Glick, K. Rossman, S. Steindorf, I.M. Maisonneuve, and J.N. Carlson. *Effects and aftereffects of ibogaine on morphine self-administration in rats.* Eur. J. Pharmacol. 195, 341 (1991). - 31 T.S.L. Cappendijk and M.R. Dzoljic, Eur. J. Pharmacol. 14, 261 (1993). Taken from Alper, Kenneth R. IBOGAINE: A REVIEW. Departments of Psychiatry and Neurology. New York University School of Medicine. New York, NY 10016: PDF Retrieved June 10, 2017

210 https://www.ibogainealliance.org/guidelines/

211 IBID

212 IBID

213 IBID

214 IBID

215 Sweetnam, P.M., J. Lancaster, A. Snowman, J.L. Collins, S. Perschke, C. Bauer & J.Ferkany. 1995. *Receptor binding profile suggests multiple mechanisms of action are responsible for ibogaine's putative anti-addictive activity.* Psychopharmacology 118: 369-376. Taken from: Deborah C. Mash,

B Craig A. Kovera, Billy E. Buck, Michael D. Norenberg, Paul Shapshak, W. Lee Hearn, Juan Sanchezramos. Medication Development of Ibogaine as a Pharmacotherapy for Drug Dependence/ Departments of Neurology, Psychiatry, Orthopedics, and Pathology, University of Miami School of Medicine, Miami, Florida 33136, USA

216 Alper, Kenneth R, M.D. Stajic, Marina Ph.D. R. Gill, JamesM.D. *Fatalities Temporally Associated with the Ingestion of Ibogaine,* J Forensic Sci, March 2012, Vol. 57, No. 2 doi: 10.1111/j.1556-4029.2011.02008.x

217 www.ibogainealliance.org/guidelines/benzodiazepines/

218 IBID

219 IBID

220 Busjahn A, Seebohm G, Maier G, Toliat MR, Nürnberg P, Aydin A, Luft FC, Lang F. *Association of the serum and glucocorticoid regulated kinase (sgk1) gene with QT interval.* Cellular Physiology and Biochemistry. 2004. Taken from: Dickinson, Jonathan. McAlpin, Jamie R.N. Wilkins, Clare. Fitzsimmons, Christine R.N. Paige, Guion R.N. Paterson, Tanea. Greene, Douglas. Chaves, Bruno Rasmussen M.D. Editors. Kamlet, Jeffrey M.D., DABAM, FASAM. Paskulin, Roman M.D., Ph.D. September 2015. *Clinical Guidelines for Ibogaine-Assisted Detoxification - The Global Ibogaine Therapy Alliance.* Retrieved February 22 2018 from https://www. ibogainealliance.org/guidelines/steroids/

221 IBID

222 IBID

223 https://www.ibogainealliance.org/guidelines/other-medications/

224 IBID

225 IBID

226 IBID

IBOGAINE SYNTHETICS

227 Glick SD, Kuehne ME, Maisonneuve IM, Bandarage UK, Molinari HH. *18-Methoxycoronaridine, a non-toxic iboga alkaloid congener: effects on morphine and cocaine self-administration and on mesolimbic dopamine release in rats.* Brain Research. May 1996;719(1):29-35.

228 Glick SD, Maisonneuve IM, Szumlinski KK. *Mechanisms of action of ibogaine: relevance to putative therapeutic effects and development of a safer iboga alkaloid congener.* Alkaloids Chem Biol 2001;56:39–53

229 http://www.savanthwp.com/about.html. Retrieved October 27, 2017

230 Hamilton, Keegan. *"Meet The Scientists Who May Have Found The Cure For Drug Addiction."* October 9, 2014. Retrieved March 10 2018 from: https://www.buzzfeed.com/keeganhamilton/the-search-for-the-antidote-to-cocaine-addiction#1las1cd

IBOGA(INE)'S LEGAL STATUS

231 Taken fromhttps://pubchem.ncbi.nlm.nih.gov/compound/Tabernanthalog. Retrieved 5 January 2020.

232 Toronto Sun. July 27, 2015. *Health Canada warns against use of health products containing ibogaine.* http://www.torontosun.com/2015/07/27/health-canada-warns-against-use-of-health-products-containing-ibogaine. Retrieved September 10, 2017

233 http://healthycanadians.gc.ca/recall-alert-rappel-avis/hc-sc/2015/54378a-eng.php. Retrieved September 25, 2017

234 http://www.logir.fo/foldb/bek/1993/0000698.htm. Retrieved September 21, 2017

235 Dumond, Julien 8 août 2006, *Mort mystérieuse lors d'une*

cure de désintoxication, Le Parisien. http://www.leparisien. fr/faits-divers/mort-mysterieuse-lors-d-une-cure-de-desin- toxication-01-08-2006-2007210839.php. Retrieved October 5 2017

236 http://www.daath.hu/incoming/66_2012_korm.rend.pdf.

237 http://www.irishstatutebook.ie/eli/2010/act/22/enacted/ en/pdf Retrieved October 10, 2017

238 http://eur-lex.europa.eu/LexUriServ/LexUriServ. do?uri=CELEX:31965L0065:EN:HTML Retrieved October 10, 2017

239 https://lovdata.no/dokument/SF/forskrift/2013-02-14-199 Retrieved October 10, 2017

240 https://www.unodc.org/pdf/research/Swedish_drug_con- trol.pdf Retrieved October 10, 2017

241 UK Home Office (2014)'Drugs:International Comparator. https://www.gov.uk/government/uploads/system/uploads/ attachment_data/file/368489/DrugsInternationalCompara- tors.pdf Retrieved October 10, 2017

242 Karolinska Institutet (2013) *HIV/HCV Co-infection in Sweden – Epidemiology, HCV Treatment and the Importance of il28b Gene Polymorphism.* https://publications.ki.se/xm- lui/bitstream/handle/10616/41788/Thesis_Jenny_Stenkvist. pdf?sequence=1 Retrieved October 10, 2017

243 https://www.admin.ch/opc/de/classified-compila- tion/19981989/index.html Retrieved October 12, 2017

244 Ikonen, Charlotte. *Fake 'experts' jailed after heroin user from Bovingdon dies in clinic.* 6th February 2017 HTTP:// www.watfordobserver.co.uk/news/15070367.Fake____ex- perts____jailed_after_heroin_user_from_Bovingdon_dies_ in_clinic. Retrieved October 10, 2017

245 U.S.C. 812 – Schedules of controlled substances. Retrieved October 15, 2017

246 http://legislature.vermont.gov/bill/status/2016/H.741. Retrieved October 9, 2017

247 https://legiscan.com/NY/text/A08356/id/1260231. Retrieved October 16, 2017

THE IBOGAINE BILL OF RIGHTS

248 Lotsof, Howard. *"Ibogaine Patient's Bill of Rights."*Retrieved August 15, 2018: from https://www.ibogainealliance.org/advocacy/bill-of-rights/

THE MODERN HISTORY OF IBOGA: A TIMELINE

249 Bowditch, Thomas Edward. *Mission from Cape Coast Castle to Ashantee, with a statistical account of that kingdom, and geographical notices of other parts of the interior of Africa*, London: J. Murray, 1819.

250 Baillon, H. *Sur l'oubouélè du Gabon (The Oubwele of Gabon). Bulletin mensuel de la Société Linéenne de Paris vol. 1(98).* 1889. P 782-783.

251 Neu, Henri (Father). *Archives générales des Pères du Saint-Esprit Vol. 148-B-i.* 1885.

252 Mitteilungen aus den Deutschen Schutzgebeiten. Volume XI 1898: 29. Taken from :Fernandez, James W. Tabernanthe Iboga. *Ecstasis and the work of the ancestors.*

253 J. Dybowsky and E. Landrin, Compt. Rend. Acad. Sci. 133, 748 (1901).

254 Pouchet, G. and Chevalier, J. 1905. *Note sur l'action pharmacologique de l'ibogaïne. Sur l'action pharmacodynamique de l'ibogaïne* (Note on the pharmacological action of ibogaine.)

255 R. Goutarel, O. Gollnhofer, and R. Sillans, Psyched. Mono. Essays 6, 70 (1993)

Retrieved February 12 from https://www.researchgate.net/publication/11650000_Chapter_1_Ibogaine_A_review

256 H. Isbell, "Ciba Ibogaine File Document No. AB0491-492 410," 1955 Retrieved May 2018 from http://www.academia. edu/30885958/The_ibogaine_medical_subculture.

257 https://patents.google.com/patent/US2813873A/en

258 Schneider, Jurg. Experiential 12:323-24, 1956

259 Taylor. W. I. *Iboga Alkaloids. II.1 the Structures of Ibogaine, Ibogamine and Tabernanthine.* J. Am. Chem. Soc., 1957, 79 (12), pp 3298–3299. 1957 Retrieved January 2018 from: https://pubs.acs.org/doi/abs/10.1021/ja01569a093

260 H.S. Lotsof, U.S. Patent 4,499,096; Chem. Abstr. 102,160426w (1985).

261 Howard Lotsof, Excerpt from the film *Ibogaine: Right of Passage*

262 G. Büchi, D.L. Coffen, K. Kocsis, P.E. Sonnet, and F.E. Ziegler, *The Total Synthesis of Iboga Alkaloids Chem. Soc. P.* 88, 3099 (1966).
Retrieved December 2017 from https://pubs.acs.org/doi/abs/10.1021/ja00965a039

263 R. Goutarel, O. Gollnhofer, and R. Sillans, Psyched. Mono. Essays 6, 70 (1993). Retrieved February 18 from https://www.researchgate.net/publication/11650000_Chapter_1_Ibogaine_A_review

264 D.P. Bocher and C. Naranjo, French Special Drug Patent No. 138.081;081713m, Inst. Class A61k (1969)

265 Freedlander, Jonathan. *Ibogaine: A Novel Anti-Addictive Compound – A Comprehensive Literature Review.* University of Maryland Baltimore County, Journal of Drug Education and Awareness, 2003; 1:79–98.

266 Alper, Kenneth R.; Beal, Dana; Kaplan, Charles D. *A Contemporary History of Ibogaine in the United States and Europe. Ibogaine: Proceedings of the First International Conference. The Alkaloids.*

267 H.S. Lotsof, U.S. Patent 4,499,096 (1985)

268 H.S. Lotsof, U.S. Patent 4,857,523 (1989)

269 H.S. Lotsof, U.S. Patent 5,026,697 (1991)

270 H.S. Lotsof, U.S. Patent 4,587,243 (1986)

271 H.S. Lotsof, U.S. Patent 5,152,994(1992)

272 Beal, Dana. De Rienzo, Paul. *The Ibogaine story: Report on the Staten Island Project*, New York, Autonomedia, 1997, P.56

273 W. van den Brink, V.M. Hendriks, P. Blanken, and J.M. van Ree, Ned Tjdschr Geneeskd. Medical prescription of heroin to treatment-resistant heroin addicts: two randomised controlled trials. P. 144, 108 (2000) Retrieved May 2 2018 from: https://www.ncbi.nlm.nih.gov/pubmed/12907482

274 Glick, S. D., Gallagher, C. A., Hough, L. B., Rossman, K. L., & Maisonneuve, I. M. (1992). *Differential effects of ibogaine pretreatment on brain levels of morphine and (+)-amphetamine. Brain Research, 588*(1), 173-176. Retrieved June 10 from http://psycnet.apa.org/record/1993-12784-001

275 T.S.L. Cappendijk and M.R. Dzoljic, Eur. J. Pharmacol. 14, 261 (1993).

276 Ravalec, Mallendi, Paicheller, *Iboga: The visionary root of African Shamanism*, P158, 159.

277 Alper, K, *Treatment of acute opioid withdrawal with ibogaine.* 1999

278 Loi n° 2/94 du 23 décembre 1994, *portant sur la protection des biens culturels* [Law No. 2/94 of 23 December 1994 on the protection of cultural property]. African Archaeology (in French). 2008. Retrieved June 2 2017 from: http://www.unesco.org/culture/natlaws/media/pdf/senghor/senghor2_droit&patr2002_freorof_engorof.pdf

279 R. Goutarel, O. Gollnhofer, and R. Sillans, Psyched. Mono. Essays 6, 70 (1993). Retrieved February 18 from: https://

www.researchgate.net/publication/11650000_Chapter_1_
Ibogaine_A_review

280 Ustanova Iboga, Retrieved November 5, 2017, from http://
www.ustanova-iboga.si

281 Freedlander, Jonathan.*Ibogaine: A Novel Anti-Addictive
Compound – A Comprehensive Literature Review.* University
of Maryland Baltimore County, Journal of Drug Education
and Awareness, 2003; 1:82–85.

282 Burne, Jerome *"One-Step Cure for Addiction?"* originally
in FOCUS MAG. Retrieved July 2018, http://www. ibo-
gaine-therapy.net/index408b.html

283 IBID

284 Glick SD, Kuehne ME, Maisonneuve IM, Bandarage UK,
Molinari HH. *"18-Methoxycoronaridine, a non-toxic iboga
alkaloid congener: effects on morphine and cocaine self-administration and on mesolimbic dopamine release in rats."*
Brain Research. May 1996;719(1):29-35. Retrieved October
10 from https://www.ncbi.nlm.nih.gov/pubmed/8782860

285 Love, S., P. Plaha, N. K. Patel, G. R. Hotton, D. J. Brooks,
and Gill, S. S. (2005) *Glial cell line-derived neurotrophic
factor induces neuronal sprouting in human brain.* Nature
Medicine 11:703-704. Retrieved September 15 from https://
www.nature.com/articles/nm0705-703

286 Glick SD, Maisonneuve IM, Szumlinski KK. *"18-Me-
thoxycoronaridine (18-MC) and ibogaine: comparison of
antiaddictive efficacy, toxicity, and mechanisms of action."*
Annals of the New York Academy of Sciences. September
2000;914(1):369-386. Retrieved March 4 from https://www.
ncbi.nlm.nih.gov/pubmed/11085336

287 Hamilton K. *Meet The Scientists Who May Have Found
The Cure For Drug Addiction.* Buzzfeed. October 9, 2014.
Retrieved August 17 from https://www.buzzfeed.com/kee-

ganhamilton/the-search-for-the-antidote-to-cocaine-addic-
tion

288 S. Witter, The Times Magazine (London), July 11, (1998).

289 Beal, Dana. De Rienzo, Paul. *The Ibogaine Story: Report on the Staten Island Project*, New York, Autonomedia, 1997

290 K.R. Alper, H.S. Lotsof, G,M,N Franken et al, "*Treatment of Acute Opioid Withdrawal with Ibogaine*," American Journal on Addictions 8 (1999): 234-42

291 Alper KR, Lotsof HS, Kaplan CD. *The ibogaine medical subculture.* J Ethnopharmacol. 2008;115(1):9-24

292 https://www.cbd.int/abs/about/

293 http://legislature.vermont.gov/bill/status/2016/H.741

294 A08356 https://legiscan.com/NY/text/A08356/id/1260231

295 Bartolotta, Devin. *Maryland Lawmakers Consider Using Ibogaine To Treat Addiction:* Retrieved August 2017 from http://baltimore.cbslocal.com/2018/02/27/maryland-ibo-gaine/

296 Epstein, Kayla. Oakland decriminalizes 'magic mushrooms' and other natural psychedelics. June 5. The Washington Post. Retrieved June 8 2019 from:

https://www.washingtonpost.com/nation/2019/06/05/oak-land-decriminalizes-magic-mushrooms-other-natural-psy-chedelics/?utm_term=.064df7f36649

297 https://pubchem.ncbi.nlm.nih.gov/compound/Tabernan-thalog

298 https://www.prnewswire.com/news-releases/mind-cure-announces-manufacturing-of-synthetic-ibo-gaine-to-be-used-in-companys-clinical-research

Made in the USA
Las Vegas, NV
04 September 2021